CW00524082

THE GILDER'S MANUAL

THE GILDER'S MANUAL;

A COMPLETE PRACTICAL GUIDE TO

GILDING IN ALL ITS BRANCHES.

DESIGNED FOR

ALL TRADES IN WHICH GILDING IS USED.

INCLUDING SILVERING.

TOGETHER WITH

PICTURE FRAMING, PICTURE REPAIRING, AND MUCH OTHER USEFUL INFORMATION, VALUABLE RECEIPTS, &c.

Entered according to act of Congress in the year 1876,
JESSE HANEY & Co., in the office of the Librarian of
Congress, at Washington.

Fredonia Books
Amsterdam, The Netherlands

The Gilder's Manual:
Complete Guide to Gilding an Silvering, Picture
Framing and Repairing

An Anonymous Author

ISBN: 1-4101-0401-X

Copyright © 2003 by Fredonia Books

Reprinted from the 1876 edition

Fredonia Books
Amsterdam, The Netherlands
http://www.fredoniabooks.com

In order to make original editions of historical works
available to scholars at an economical price, this
facsimile of the original edition of 1876 is
reproduced from the best available copy and has
been digitally enhanced to improve legibility, but the
text remains unaltered to retain historical
authenticity.

THE GILDER'S MANUAL

THE GILDER'S MANUAL.

PICTURE FRAME GILDING,

AND

Gilding for Interior Decoration.

PREPARATIONS USED IN GILDING.

WE shall first describe the various preparations used by the gilder, and would here mention the importance of having clean pots and brushes, and of being particular to keep all preparations from dust and dirt. This is necessary if the operator wishes to accomplish beautiful and brilliant work. We shall give the best description of how the work is to be performed, and the latest and best practical recipes known to the trade.

PARCHMENT SIZE.—The size used by gilders in England is made from parchment cuttings, or cuttings from gloves. In America there is a white glue in use, which is not so fine or suitable for the work. Parchment size is made by first washing as many cuttings as you have room for in a clean stone pipkin cover them with water, and let them simmer for two hours, when, to test if it is boiled enough, the inside of the palm of the hand should be slightly wetted with the size, and the other hand pressed closely several times upon it, when if it be found to be *sticky*, the size may be poured off into a clean basin to cool for use. This size is most important to the gilder, as he uses it to mix nearly all his preparations in the practice of his art. When it is cool, it is like jelly, and the stronger the size the firmer it will be. The bottom and top of the basin of size will be found not so pure or transparent as the middle, and the gilder is always particular to mix his *burnish* and *matt* with the finest and clearest size, while the tops and bottoms go to mix whitening, stopping, thick white, &c. If the size is too thick it will be necessary to add water in making up some of the preparations, and as the strength of size is important, we shall refer to it again shortly.

OIL GOLD SIZE.—This size is a mixture of boiled linseed oil and ochre, well ground up together. The carver and gilder seldom, if ever, make this size for use, as it can be purchased cheaply by weight. It is too solid for use as kept in stock, and is thinned down with boiled oil to about the consistence of cream.

MATT GOLD SIZE.—This also is purchased of artists' colormen by weight. It is of a chocolate color, and very stiff. When it is required for use a small portion of parchment size is put into a stone pot, and about twice the quantity of water; when the size is melted into the water, a small portion of the matt gold size is added, and stirred till it is dissolved; more is added till it is of the consistence of thick cream. This preparation is obliged to be used warm, as the size with which it is mixed would coagulate.

BURNISH GOLD SIZE.—Like the preceeding, this is usually bought of the artists' colorman, and is mixedl ike the above. It does not pay to make this article, but the following ingredients ground together very finely would bring out a good burnish. Black lead, deer suet, and red chalk, one ounce each, with one pound of pipe clay, ground with parchment size to a stiff paste. This size is made ready for use like matt.

CLAY.—This preparation is usually bought of the artists' colorman, and is mixed the same as burnish size.

GILDER'S ORMOLU.—This preparation is mixed with thin parchment size, to give the oil and matt gilding a deeper and richer appearance. To medium strength parchment size add enough of the following recipe to color it. It is better strained before putting into the size, and applied like a varnish, thinly and carefully.

Recipe.—Mix together one-fourth pint of spirits of wine, half ounce of unbleached shellac, one dram red Saunder's wood, half dram tumeric. Shake every now and then until completely dis solved.

STOPPING.—This is a mixture of size and whitening to the consistence of putty. It is used for stopping up holes, or making up defects in the work.

THICK WHITE.—This is a mixture of whitening and parchment size to the consistence of cream, and is put on the parts to be burnished previous to the burnish size.

WHITENING.—The whitening used by the trade is usually bought in 100 pound barrels, and is a very superior article to that used in the household, as there is no grit in it, and the gilder is particular to protect the whitening barrel from dust. Before being used for the various preparations, it is rolled out on a board with a rolling pin until it is perfectly smooth and fine.

WHITENING UP.—Nearly all the work undertaken by the gilder,

especially that of picture and looking-glass frames, requires to have a foundation of whitening and size ; the reason is that it can be got up much more smoothly; and a brilliant burnish can only be produced on a good foundation of whitening. For outside work paint is used as a foundation, and the gilding is invariably done in oil, as no other gilding would stand the weather. It is therefore important that whitening up various moldings and articles should be practiced by the learner. It must be remembered that all the stock moldings kept by the professional gilder comes to hand ready whitened up from the manufactory, and there they have a ready method of whitening up with templets, which renders the moldings cheaper. The gilder has oftentimes frames to make to pattern, when he has to get the molding made, and then whiten it up.

The first thing to be done is to give the molding a priming of *thin white*, composed of parchment size and whitening, and laid on *very hot*. After this is dry, the irregularities and defects of the molding are filled up with *stopping*, and then *thick white* is evenly laid on with a brush. As before observed, the *thick white* is made by increasing the quantity of whitening to a gives amount of size till it is about the consistence of thick cream. When several coats of *thick white* have been laid on, each one being dry before the next is applied, *pumice stone* of various shapes to fit is applied to the beads, hollows, flats, &c., giving the work a coat of white at the same time, and well rubbing down all the rough projections in the molding, and also taking care to well square up all the angles in the various members of the molding. In smoothing it out, superfluous whitening will be rubbed out by the pumice stone, which must be taken off.

After repeated smoothing down, it is finished off with clean water, when it will be found to be smooth. The thickness of whitening on the wood should be one-sixteenth of an inch, and in some instances thicker. Care should be taken not to use the whitening and size when it is beginning to "turn off," as it then loses a great part of its adhesive quality. Different strengths must also be guarded against, as a strong coat of whitening size laid on a weak foundation will be likely to peel up when the after preparations are laid on.

GILDING.

There are two kinds of gilding practiced by the trade; one is called "oil gilding," the other "water gilding;" and the latter is both matt and burnish. Moldings full of small members, and work full of ornaments, are generally gilt in oil, while broad flat surfaces and plain beads and hollows are gilt in water, and sometimes in oil. Matt and burnish gilding are seen on the same molding or piece of work.

In the chapter on composition ornaments we describe the method of getting out, fixing on, and backing up the corners on frames, but have hitherto said nothing on mitering-up moldings, which will be done shortly; and our first essay at gilding will be on an ornamental frame of broad molding, mounted with corners, and will be in "oil."

OIL GILDING.

After the corners have been backed up and hardened by being in a dry place, the first care of the gilder is to wash the ornaments on the frame to free them from the oil and dust that may cover them in getting them out of the mold and on to the frame. After this is dry, the coat of *thin white* is evenly put on the frame. When this is dry, *stopping* is used to fill up the holes and defects in the molding, and to square up the corners that are damaged, and make good all ornaments that are chipped. When the stopping is hardened, the frame is ready for glass papering, and the back edge, hollows, beads, and flat parts of the frame are perfectly smoothed with *fine* glass paper. This is important, if good work is required to be turned out. Glass paper for the gilder's use is cut up into pieces about two inches square, and the sizes most generally used are No. 2, 1½, 1, 0. No very coarse glass paper is required. After well brushing out the frame with the *dusting brush*, it is ready for two coats of thin white mixed with clay. When this is dry, it is ready for again carefully fine glass papering, and is then ready for what is technically termed *clear cole*. This is parchment size thinned down with water moderately, and put on warm. The object of thus sizing the work is to keep the next coat, which will be oil, from sinking into the surface. Two coats of this size are usually laid on, and it is much better to lay on two or more coats of weak than one of strong size, as the latter sometimes, if too strong, peals off. Size that has been kept a little too long, and commenced running or spoiling, is known to make first rate *clear cole*. After the size is dry, the frame will be ready for oil and the workman mixes enough oil gold size to about the consistence of cream, and strains it through some clean linen rag screwed up tightly, forcing out the oil size. This oil gold size is laid on the frame very thinly and evenly with a brush. The thinner it is laid on the better but great care much be exercised to touch the whole of the surface of the molding, and to be most particular to brush in the oil to the bottom of the work. It is usual to put work in oil the last thing at night, so that it may be ready for gilding the first thing in the morning. It is known to be ready for gilding by the oil being *just tackey*, and *nearly dry*, and in this state the gold will adhere firmly, and brush off bright; but if the oil has been laid on too thick, or the gold applied when it is too tackey or not dry enough, it will be dull, and greater care must be exercised in *skewing* in the gold, or the more prominent parts will have the metal brushed from the surface.

The frame being ready, the gilder blows the gold out on the cushion, and cuts the sheet of gold up into convenient sized pieces to suit the various parts of the frame, and takes them up with the *tip*, and lays them on the frame till it is well covered with gold. In a frame gilded in oil the gold is ragged, and in many places of double and treble thickness. The gold is first carefully pressed down with a *dabber*, and then skewed well in with a *badger*. A rather long-haired brush set in quill is used, called a *skewing brush*, to brush out and off the frame the old skewings remaining. After this operation, the frame is ready for *finish size*. This is clear size, rather weak, laid on evenly with a hog's-hair brush, and if it is thought desirable to deepen the color of the gold, a little *ormolu* is added in order to give it a deeper and richer color.

The *skewings*, which are the small particles of gold not required on the frame, are carefully put away and sold to the gold beater when a sufficient quantity has been collected.

The frame will now be complete when the back edge is brushed over with yellow ochre, mixed with size.

WATER AND OIL GILDING.

After going through the operation of gilding a frame in oil, which is comparatively simple, the reader will be prepared to gild a more elaborate frame, finished with brilliant burnish on the corners, beads, &c., and a broad *double gilt* flat and hollow on the inside. It may be mentioned here, all the best work that is flat, such as broad insides to picture frames, spandrills, flat looking-glass frames, &c., are double gilt; and this is done to give the work a better color and more solid appearance.

Some of the gilder's customers may perhaps think he overcharges a little for his work, but when he is anxious to please his customer with good work, it should be borne in mind both gold and time must be paid for that have contributed to the result.

We will now describe the operation of gilding a broad frame made of Alhambra molding, with corners and a broad flat inside. As a general rule the broad flat insides to frames are made separate, and fit into the rabbet of the outside frame when made. This is convenient to the gilder, as he gilds the flat in water apart from the frame it is made to fit.

The first thing the workman is careful to do is to see that the frame is free from dust, dirt, or grease; and if not, to wash the frame with a brush and clean water, care being taken not to take off the sharpness of the ornaments in the operation. After it is dry, a coat of *thin white* is then applied, and then all holes, &c., are made good by *stopping*, and the parts to be burnished receive three or four coats of *thick white*. When the last coat of thick white is nearly dry, pass over the parts with the finger, which will help to smooth the rough surfaces. It may perhaps puzzle a novice what parts should be burnished in various descriptions of work, but a good rule will be to take the most prominent plain parts of the ornaments and the beads; and in the case of scrolls on a chimney glass, the scrolls fixed on for burnishing should be followed throughout with burnish. It requires taste and judgment to so distribute the burnish in any work that it may not be overdone and lose its effect, but judiciously placed, so that the *matted* portions will stand in strong contrast, and produce brilliant work. The frame is then carefully and thoroughly glass-papered till it is smooth, when it receives a coat of thin white mixed with clay, and is again glass-papered and brushed down. Two coats of *clear cole*, evenly laid on, follow, taking care that the first coat is thoroughly dry before the second is laid on. When this is done the frame is put in oil, in the same way as before mentioned, and afterward all the beads and ornaments which have received the coats of thick white, and selected for burnishing, must be rubbed clean of every particle of oil. This is usually done by wetting a piece of calico, and wringing it out; commence by putting it round the second finger of the right hand, and pass it carefully over the parts to be burnished, changing the surface of the calico on the finger very often. Should any of the other parts of the frame be touched by the damp calico, it will be necessary to again apply the oil brush to remedy the accident, and a small camel's hair brush will sometimes be needed to touch in small imperfections. Although it is thought that every particle of grease has been wiped off, yet it is necessary the next morning, before laying the gold, to go over all the parts gone over with the damp linen with *clay*. This is done to prevent the possibility of any gold adhering, as it would have to be glass-papered off before putting on more preparation. The frame is then gilded as before described, and the gold skewed into the bottoms of the ornaments; after which, if there are any "faults" in the gilding, they can be rectified by taking a small camel's hair brush, and wetting it in the mouth, apply the moist brush to the spot, and lay gold enough to cover it. The frame must then be *finish sized* once, as before mentioned.

We must now look to the burnishes, left with a coat of *clay*. Matt gold size must be mixed, and three or four coats must be evenly applied with a camel's hair brush. When dry, it should be gone over with a damp sponge. On this surface lay two coats of *burnish gold size* as evenly as possible, when it will be ready for the gold as soon as the last coat is dry. We must now lay the gold on these burnishes in a different manner from that mentioned before, and we will first gild the bead running round the frame between the parts already gilded in oil. The frame is raised on the left hand, so as to be at an inclination, to allow the surplus water to run off, when we must be provided with a clean glass of water and camel's hair pencils, and must proceed to work in the following manner : A convenient sized camel's hair pencil that will cover the bead is dipped in the water, and scraped over the edge of the glass, and beginning at the left hand end of the bead, proceed to wet the bead for five or six inches down, and pass the brush over it till it is thorougly soaked; and while the water is yet floating on the bead, the strip of gold, which is ready on the *tip*, must be laid quickly and evenly.

It may as well be mentioned that with water gilding the gold cushion is held as usual in the left hand, and the knife and tip are held between the fingers beneath. The workman commences by cutting strips of gold leaf the necessary width, and taking up one on his tip, it is put between the fingers of the left hand till the bead is ready to receive the gold; the brush is placed in the glass; and the tip, ready with gold leaf, is taken from between the fingers, and the gold applied; after which another strip of gold is taken up on the tip, and it is returned to its place between the fingers of the left hand to wait till another piece of the bead is soaked, and ready to receive it. This operation is continued till the whole of the bead is covered; also the burnish in the corners, &c., must in the same way be covered. It is scarcely necessary to mention that the water must be kept from the gilded portions of the frame as much as possible. In laying a bead, it will be better to have no uneven edges to the gold where it joins, as it will make it more solid and save trouble. Should there be a defect in the gold caused by laying on or other causes, it must quickly be made good by applying more gold lightly to the spot.

The whole of the frame is now covered with gold, and the beads and ornaments just laid must remain till they are dry, which will be perhaps two hours, unless the workman is in a warm shop.

Burnishing out the gold thus laid is the next operation, and is thus performed : The burnisher, which is usually curved at the end, is grasped in the right hand, and the curved part applied to the work; with a slight pressure from the thumb of the left hand, which also steadies the tool, the burnisher is rubbed steadily backward and forward, when it will be found to bring up a brilliant burnish. Sometimes the burnisher is used at the point to burnish close up to the ornaments, and for hollows, &c. Burnishers of various sizes and shapes are used for the work ; a little practice will enable the learner to soon find out the best shapes for the work in hand.

The frame in hand must now be looked carefully over, and if any "faults" occur round the base of any of the burnished ornaments, which is sometimes the case, it must be made good as before described, and the frame again finish sized, care being taken not to touch the burnished parts with size, when the work may be said to be finished so far, after the edge has been yellowed with ochre.

The broad inside flat and hollow must now be taken in hand, and as an engraving is to be put into the frame when it is finished, we must burnish the hollow; but if an oil painting had been going into the finished frame, the hollow would not have been burnished. We make this a rule, as the burnished hollow next to a painting disturbs the eye, which ought to rest in repose on the picture; but with an engraving with a broad white margin, the burnished hollow gives a more finished appearance to the whole, and the white margin keeps the eye from wandering.

The inside flat and hollow is about one and a half inches wide, and in order to make it look well it must be carefully prepared up, and double gilt in water. Large flat surfaces tax the gilder's skill, so as to make the whole look solid, without an appearance of a join in the gold. Sometimes the miters require rubbing down with pumice stone and water if they have not been neatly joined, and then any inequalities in the surface hollow or edge neatly *stopped*, and when dry carefully rubbed down with rather fine *glass paper*, when a coat of *clay* is evenly put on, and it is again *glass papered*, rubbed down, and four coats of matt gold size smoothly put on, when it is again glass papered and washed carefully down with a piece of cloth. When this is nearly dry, take a piece of dry cloth and briskly rub over the flat, when a polished surface will be the result. On this surface lay two coats of *weak size*, and when dry it is ready for the first layer of gold. As our inside flat is one and a half inches broad, the gold leaf will have to be cut one leaf in two. Proceed as before stated for water gilding, taking care *not* to lay the gold in the hollow. When the gold is laid all round, the work must be hung up until quite dry, which may be three or four hours according to the temperature of the room. When dry, take a piece of cotton wool, the finest is sold by druggists, and rub off the superfluous gold, when it is possible a lot of *faults* in the gold will be discovered, and perhaps what is called "spiders' legs" will be seen; but as our work is to have another layer of gold, this difficulty will be got over. After the superfluous gold is rubbed off, a coat of *weak size* must be put on the gold, and when dry two coats of *burnish gold size* in the hollow; when dry the work is ready for the second coat of gold, which must be laid on as before, taking care, on this occasion, to lay the hollow with the flat. When dry, the hollow must be *burnished* carefully with a burnisher, taking care the tool does not slip over the matt, as it will make a scratch that cannot be easily got out. When the matt has received two coats of finish size, the inside may be said to be finished.

The tyro must remember never to touch his burnishes with size or water, and hence arises the necessity of sometimes being obliged to change the order of the processes to save the burnishes from damage.

The *faults* spoken of will be found to have disappeared with the laying of the second layer of gold, but if there should be a fault it must be seen to *before* the finish size is laid on, or it will show very badly, and spoil what would otherwise be considered good work.

WHITE AND GOLD.

In many of the best drawing rooms of the present day suites of furniture in white and gold are used, and nothing looks so chaste where the surrounding colors harmonize.

This class of work requires great care in whitening up and preparing; also taste and judgment to decide what parts of the article should be white, matt, or burnish. Brackets, whatnots, console tables, chairs, lounges, and many other articles of furniture are ordered in white and gold; and we will here describe the process on a carved chair, when, if the directions are followed with any carved article, the result will be satisfactory.

Chairs are oftentimes delivered into the gilder's hands whitened up, but where this is not done it is necessary to carefully whiten up the article, being particular to draw up the whitening so that every part of the pattern shall be sharp, and stand out well in bold relief, according to the directions before given on whitening up.

As the back and seat of our chair are to be needlework it will be necessary to see that they both fit in their proper places, so that the gilding may not be damaged when finished.

After glass papering, we must decide on the parts to white, burnish, and matt, when a coat of *clay* must be applied to all the parts required to be gilt, care being taken not to go over the parts decided on to be white, and the work will proceed in the same way as laid down for water gilding.

When all the gold is laid and burnished out, and the matt *finish sized*, the white parts must receive two or three coats of *flake white* and parchment size, not too thick, care being taken to give a clean finish to the gilding in passing over it with a camel's hair brush.

If the work is ordered to be varnished, it will be necessary to give the white two coats of clear size to prevent the varnish from sinking in, when the chair will be ready to receive a coat of enamel white varnish. With this operation the white will become a cream color.

Articles are sometimes got up in mauve and other delicate colors to suit the taste of the purchaser. Where silver leaf is required to be laid, the process will be the same as for gold leaf.

Cheap gilding, so called, consists in laying silver leaf, or even tin foil, instead of gold leaf, and then varnishing with a "gold coloring varnish," for a recipe of which see toward the close of this volume.

LOOKING-GLASS FRAMES.

During the latter half of the last century the frames for looking glasses were of a set and decided pattern, and were, generally speaking, more architectural in their character than they have since been. There was a broad cornice on the top, with a frieze below it, on which was represented some allegorical subject; the sides consisted of a column or pillar on a flat ground. The Corinthian order was sometimes adopted, and terminated with capitals and bases of the same; square blocks were placed under the base, and the cornice was supported by the capital. This style was succeeded by doing away with the molding and frieze, and substituting a column of the same order as the sides. Not half a century ago the columns were dispensed with altogether. The sides and top of the frame were made of equal width, and consisted of a flat ground, bounded at each edge by a hollow or some other small molding, and the corners were ornamented by carved or composition ornaments.

The next style may be called the "modern antique," in which

the style of the times of Charles II., Anne, and Louis XIV. pre-
vailed.

At the present time glass frames are made of every description and style, so that any style of furniture can be matched,
either mediæval or modern.

There are two shapes, technically called "landscape" and
"pier." The "*landscape*" glass is long, and the "*pier*" is upright.

Although any size can be made to order, yet the following
are standard sizes, and frames are kept in stock of the following
sizes rabbet measure :

PIER.

40 in. high by 30 in. broad.	60 in. high by 48 in. broad
44 in. high by 34 in. broad.	70 in. high by 44 in. broad.
50 in. high by 40 in. broad.	70 in. high by 50 in. broad.
54 in. high by 44 in. broad.	70 in. high by 30 in. broad.
56 in. high by 44 in. broad.	76 in. high by 48 in. broad.

LANDSCAPE.

40 in. broad by 30 in. high.	40 in. broad by 36 in. high.
44 in. broad by 34 in. high.	50 in. broad by 40 in. high.

COMPOSITION ORNAMENTS.

The ornaments with which gold frames are mounted are of
comparatively recent date, having first come into use about a
century ago for figures on chimney pieces, and since for picture
frames.   The ornaments are made from a mixture, for which the
following recipe will be found to answer well; any quantity can
be made in the following proportions :

RECIPE FOR COMPO.

Boil seven pounds of the best glue in seven half pints of water,
melt three pounds of best rosin in three pints of raw linseed oil.
When the ingredients are well boiled, put them into a large
vessel and simmer them for half an hour, stirring it, and taking
care it does not boil over.   When this is done, pour the mixture
into a large quantity of whiting, previously *sifted* and rolled
very fine, and mix it to the consistence of dough, and it is ready
for molding into the required shapes.   The above compo will
keep for a long time in a damp place, or in a barrel of whitening.

Compo, when cold, is very hard, and when required to be used it is heated by means of steam, when it assumes the consistence of dough.

The ornaments are made by pressing the compo into *molds*. The molds are made of boxwood, and the required ornament is countersunk in the wood by a man who is by trade a mold cutter.

They are got out in the following manner :

The workman takes the *mold* and well brushes into it oil and turpentine, to prevent the composition adhering to it. When composition enough, in a warm soft condition, is rolled up in the hands into a convenient form to go into the mold, it is pressed into every part very carefully by the fingers, and then a board or flat surface of iron is wetted and placed on the compo still outside the mold, when the whole is put into an iron screw press, and the pressure, which is but for a few moments, drives the compo into all the deep parts of the mold, and makes the board adhere to the back of the composition. When it is taken out of the press, the mold is removed from the ornament. After the compo has hardened a little, the ornament is cut off, and the remaining compo sliced off to be again heated and used. The ornament, when first cut off, is very soft and pliable, and can be then fitted to frames having beads hollows, &c., without fear of breaking. These ornaments are fixed on with glue, and if corners to a frame, are sometimes supported with a piece of compo behind to secure them in the position required. When dry they are quite hard and brittle, and are then to be *backed up*, that is, the spaces between the corner and the frame filled up with compo softened in hot water, which will make the ornament strong and thicker than before. The mounting of these ornaments oftentimes requires skill and practice, as they have to be placed on a large proportion of the gilded articles sold in the trade. Some of the ornaments when made require supporting in other ways besides that mentioned, as in the case of distinct fronds of ferns, a wire has to be placed throughout the back of the ornament, and secured by covering or backing up with compo, when it is found this beautiful but fragile pattern will wear well. Brackets, cornices, frames, whatnots, &c., each require the ornaments mounted so as to be graceful and suitable to the design.

For cheaper work there are gilded lead ornaments sold at twenty-five cents per pound by wholesale molding dealers.

The carver and gilder has a stock of molds to suit the various descriptions of work. As we have remarked, the molding manufacturer has facilitated the work of the carver and gilder, as the moldings come to hand ready mounted with composition ornaments, so that in many instances the picture frame, when made, only requires suitable compo corners Where looking glass frames are made, they are mounted with handsome scrolls, &c., except where the pattern required is heavy and unsuitable for compo work, when, as mentioned before, the scroll pattern is carved out of soft wood, and whitened up.

On very large frames the ornaments are sometime *papier maché*, which is much lighter. These ornaments are made out of paper pulp, which is pressed between two molds, and the ornament, when pressed comes out thin and hollow. One advantage of these ornaments is that, if let fall, they are not so liable to break as compo.

These ornaments are not held in favorable estimation by the gilder, as the paper pulp does not form such a good foundation for gilding as wood or composition.

FRENCH OIL GILDING FOR PICTURE FRAMES AND INTERIOR DECORATIONS.

Oil Gilding is employed, with varnish polish, upon carriages, mirror-frames, and other furniture. The following method is employed by eminent gilders at Paris.

1. White lead, with half its weight of yellow ochre, and a little litharge, are separately ground very fine ; and the whole is then tempered with linseed oil, thinned with spirits of turpentine, and applied in an even coat, called *impression.*

2. When this coat is quite dry, several coats of best flake white very finely ground with raw linseed oil and thinned for use with spirits of turpentine as it is used, called hard tint are given, even so many as 10 or 12, should the surface require it, for smoothing and filling up the pores. These coats are given daily, leaving them to dry in the interval in a warm sunny exposure.

3. When the work is perfectly dry, it is first softened down with pumice stone and water, afterward with worsted cloth and very finely powdered pumice, till the *hard tint* gives no reflection, and is smooth as glass.

4. With a camel's hair brush, there must be given lightly and with a gentle heat, from 4 to 5 coats at least, and even sometimes double that number, of fine shellac varnish.

5. When these are dry, the grounds of the panels and the carved parts must be first polished with shave-grass ; and next with putty of tin and tripoli, tempered with water, applied with woolen cloth ; by which the varnish is polished till it shines like a mirror.

6. The work thus polished is carried into a hot place free from dust, where it receives very lightly and smoothly a thin

coat of *gold color*, much softened down. This is merely the dregs of the colors, ground and tempered with oil, which remain in the little dish in which painters clean their brushes. This substance is extremely rich and gluey ; after being ground up, and passed through fine linen cloth, it forms the ground for gold leaf. This coat is passed over it with a clean soft brush, and the thinner it is the better.

7. Whenever the gold color is dry enough to take the gold, which is ascertained by laying the back of the hand on a corner of the frame work, the gilding is begun and finished as usual.

8. The gold is smoothed off with a very soft brush, one of camel's hair, for example, of three fingers' breadth ; after which it is left to dry for several days.

9. It is then varnished with a spirit of wine varnish, and then treated with the chafing dish as follows: The workman with a lighted chafing dish holds the flame near the gilding for a moment and then passes on. He must not stop any length of time at any one spot or he will spoil the work. This gives a fine luster to the varnish coat, as it melts the small upward projections and brush marks down to a perfect dead level.

10. When this varnish is dry, two or three coats of copal or oil varnish are applied, at intervals of two days.

11. Finally, the panels are polished with a worsted cloth, with tripoli and water, and luster is given by friction with the palm of the hand, previously softened with a little olive oil, taking care not to rub off the gold.

FRENCH BURNISH GILDING.

Gilding in distemper of the French, is the same as our burnished or water gilding. Their process seems to be very elaborate, and the best consists of 17 operations ; each of them said to be essential.

1. *Encollage*, or the *glue coat*. To a decoction of wormwood and garlic in water, strained through a cloth, a little common salt and some vinegar are added. This composition, as being destructive of worms in wood, is mixed with as much good glue ; and the mixture is spread in a hot state, with a brush of boar's hair. When plaster or marble is to be gilded, the salt must be left out of the above composition, as it is apt to attract humidity in damp places, and to come out as a white powder on the gilding. But the salt is indispensable for wood. The first glue coating is made thinner than the second.

2. *White preparation.* This consists in covering the above surface with 8, 10, or 12 coats of Spanish white, mixed up with

strong size, each well worked on with the brush and in some measure incorporated with the preceding coat, to prevent their peeling off in scales.

3. *Stopping up* the pores, with thick whiting and glue, and smoothing the surface with dog-skin.

4. Polishing the surface with pumice-stone and very cold water.

5. *Reparation ;* in which a skillful artist repairs all defects.

6. *Cleansing ;* with a damp linen rag, and then a soft sponge.

7. *Preler.* This is rubbing with *shave-grass* the parts to be yellowed, in order to make them softer.

8. *Yellowing.* With this view *yellow ochre* is carefully ground in water, and mixed with transparent colorless size. The thinner part of this mixture is applied hot over the white surface with a fine brush, which gives it a fine yellow hue.

9. *Ungraining* consists in rubbing the whole work with shave-grass, to remove any granular appearance.

10. *Coat of assiette; trencher coat.* This is the composition on which the gold is to be laid. It is composed of Armenian bole, 1 pound ; oxide of iron (best red chalk or jeweler's rouge), 2 ounces ; and as much plumbago ; each separately ground in water. The whole are then mixed together, and ground up with about a spoonful of olive oil. The *assiette* well made and applied gives beauty to the gilding. The *assiette* is tempered with a white sheep skin glue, very clear and well strained. This mixture is heated and applied in three successive coats, with a very fine long-haired brush.

Rubbing, with a piece of dry, clean linen cloth ; except the parts to be burnished, which are to receive two more coats of *assiette* tempered with glue.

12. *Gilding.* The surface, being damped with cold water (iced in summer), has then the gold leaf applied to it. The hollow grounds must always be gilded before the prominent parts. Water is dexterously applied by a soft brush, immediately behind the gold leaf, before laying it down, which makes it lie smoother. Any excess of water is then removed with a dry brush.

13. *Burnishing* with bloodstone.

14. *Deadening.* This consists in passing a thin coat of glue, slightly warmed, over the parts that are not to be burnished.

15. *Mending ;* that is moistening any broken points with a brush, and applying bits of gold leaf to them.

16. The *vermeil* coat. Vermeil is a liquid which gives luster and fire to the gold ; and makes it resemble *ormolu.* It is composed as follows : 2 ounces of annotto, 1 ounce of gamboge, 1

ounce of vermilion, half an ounce of dragon's blood, 2 ounces of salt of tartar, and 18 grains of saffron, are boiled in a litre (2 pints English) of water, over a slow fire, till the liquid be reduced to a fourth. The whole is then passed through a silk or muslin sieve. A little of this is made t glide lightly over the gold, with a very soft brush.

17. *Repassage* is passing over the dead surfaces a second coat of deadening glue, which must be hotter than the first. This finishes the work, and gives it strength.

RE-GILDING.

The large variety of articles supplied new by the trade in the course of time require renovation and re-gilding, but this process differs but little from that of gilding a new article in the white. There are a few things necessary to look to, not generally required in new work, and we will now mention them

If the article required to be re-gilt is the frame of a chimney glass, the back must be carefully taken out, and the wedges holding the glass in its place must be removed, taking care they do not touch or scratch the back of the glass, and the glass taken out. Take off the ornaments on the top and the sides, if they are not compo, taking notice how again to secure them in their place. The ornaments are put on with screws from the back of the frame, or with brads and needle points. Dust well down both frame and ornaments, and be particular to see well to the rabbet that no particles of quicksilver remain, as any quicksilver coming in contact with your newly-gilt frame will turn the gold black.

Proceed to wash off all the old gold, and shell up any of the preparation that is not firm ; also ornaments that may be loose on the back or sight edge of the frame. A piece of cloth will be found to be the best thing to clean off the old gold, as there is more friction than in a sponge, but the sponge will be useful when the gold is removed to carefully go over the frame. If the frame has been varnished or gilt in oil, glass paper must be used till all the gold is removed, when a slight wash over to remove all the remaining particles of dust will be advisable. If in washing the frame you find any of the preparation blister up, you will know it is bad, and the parts blistered must be scraped off down to the wood, and when dry a coat of *thin* white of medium strength applied. Of course these remarks will be applicable to the ornaments as well as the frame ; and if you whiten the backs of the ornaments, be particular not to let any run on to the front; if it should do so, see that it is removed before it is dry, or smooth it down.

Glue on to the backs of the ornaments some blocks of wood about an inch high, when they will be found most useful in keeping the work from rubbing on the bench, and also to catch hold of in laying on the preparations and gold. The ornaments and frame are now ready for *stopping*, and making good all deficiencies, either in ornaments or preparation, and when the stopping is dry to glass paper over, and give another coat of *thin white*, and then the parts to be burnished should have three or four coats of thick white with a camel's hair brush. The frame will now go on the same as new work before mentioned until it is finished.

If the work under hand be picture frames where the ornaments are broken and lost, they must be made good. Sometimes this can be accomplished by softening compo, and putting it on to the part deficient, and with the *modelers* fashion it out to match the other ornaments. But where the pattern is small and difficult to imitate, the usual method is to take a model as follows :—

TO TAKE A MODEL IN COMPO.

If it is found necessary, in making or repairing, to replace broken ornaments on a frame, it is often a saving of time to take a model of the ornament required from a good one still remaining on the frame. Sometimes a strip of running leaf is deficient on the back or sight edge, when a piece long enough for our purpose shells up from the frame. If the ornament is loose from the frame, glue it down on a flat piece of wood, and tack round it, leaving a margin, slips of wood about half an inch high, and with the brush used for oiling the wood molds, oil the inside and the ornament, Warm the compo, and then with the fingers well squeeze in enough compo to fill the place. When it is hardened, the mold may be removed from the ornament, and a good mold will be found to be the result, from which, (when thoroughly hardened), as many ornaments may be made, in the same way as before described for the wood molds, as are wanted. If only part of an ornament is required, it is cut to the required size, and either put in or stuck on and backed up as the case may be.

If the ornament to be molded is on the frame, it will not oftentimes be found necessary or convenient to have slips of wood to keep the compo from spreading, as, if a good lump of compo is used, a mold can be made good enough for the purpose by proceeding as before mentioned. This method will be found to answer to replace ornaments on any article where the compo ornaments require mending or replacing, but where there is no ornament left to mold from, oftentimes molds that you have in stock will answer the purpose ; if not, suitable ornaments must be ordered from the dealers.

LEAF GILDING ON BRASS.

It is necessary to say a few words on gilding brass articles, as they occassionally come to the gilder to renovate.

The brass ends of cornice poles, ornaments, the ornamental brass on cabinets, and a variety of small articles are sent to the local gilder, and these articles can be done up on the premises without sending them to be re-lacquered, and will look much better and last as long.

First wash the brass ornaments in strong soda and water, well brushing out the bottoms : and when clean and dry, go over them with French polish laid on with a brush. Put the ornaments " in oil " in the usual way and gild, when they will be found to look a good color, and the gold will not be liable to scratch off. The thin coat of French polish* has been found to be a good foundation for the gold, as there is no shelling up. Where the articles are required to bear a brilliant burnish they had better be re-lacquered.

TO FROST A CARDBOARD MOUNT IN GOLD OR SILVER.

Mounts to be frosted should be made out of stout cardboard, so that the preparations laid on do not cause it to warp.

Give the mount first two coats of thin parchment size, and when dry a good coat of oil gold size. Throw on in sufficient quantity, fine, middle, or coarse emery to well cover the surface, (as you may want the frosting coarse or fine), and allow the surplus not adhering to the oil to roll off again. Lay the mount flat till the morning, or till the emery is fast on the surface. There should then be a coat of whitening and size lightly laid on, so as not to disturb the emery, and when it is dry a coat of *clay* and another coat of oil gold size, and left till the following morning, when gold or silver leaf may be laid, and finish sized. These mounts are very effective for portraits or other small works of art.

* See page 134,

TO GILD OAK AND OTHER HARD WOOD.

It is sometimes required to gild the bare wood, so as to show the grain. This may be done to look very well with oak and other hard wood, but with soft wood the grain would rise, and present a very rough appearance.

Well glass paper down the surface to be gilt, and apply two coats of strong parchment size, and when dry, oil gold size. The gold can be laid when this is nearly dry, and will brush off bright.

The above is suitable for the bevels of oak Oxford frames, screens, church decorations, and any hard wood.

TO GILD A CARDBOARD MOUNT.

Lay on three coats of matt, and lightly wash and rub down with a piece of cloth to get a perfectly smooth surface; weak size, and gild according to instruction in water gilding.

The mount to be gilt should be made of stout cardboard.

GILDING PLASTER CASTS, BRACKETS, &C.

Fasten a pledget of tow or a piece of sponge to the end of a stick; immerse it in olive oil, and daub the cast plentifully with it; in two hours this will be absorbed; the operation must be repeated again and again until the plaster is saturated to such a degree that it ceases to absorb the oil readily; then leave the cast in a dry place for twenty-four hours. With a soft brush lay a thin and even coating of thin glue (made of the best white) over the whole surface. Again leave it to dry; then have ready japanner's gold size and sufficient gold leaf. When the cast or bracket is perfectly dry, coat a portion of it evenly, and not too thickly, with the gold size; and when that is nearly dry, (which will, under ordinary circumstances, be in about ten minutes), apply the gold leaf, previously cutting it into pieces of the re quisite size, or laying it on where practicable by the page. After carefully gilding the whole, dust away superfluous bits with a clean dry, soft brush, and burnish portions here and there with a hook-shaped pettle, or agate burnisher. When durability is desired, rather than brilliancy of effect apply a coat of copal varnish.

GILDING FOR SIGNS ON WOOD.

SIZES FOR GILDING SIGNS ON WOOD.

Before considering this branch of the sign painter's art it will be best to treat upon the various sizes in general use among them.

Let every painter make his own size, and then he will be less likely to be a stranger to what he wants. If it be too slow in drying, or if it dries too quickly, he will be able to know what is required to make it right.

An excellent size is made by putting boiled oil in a good stone pot ; place it upon a slow fire, and let it rise to such a heat as nearly to ignite ; then with a match or bit of lighted paper set fire to it, and let it burn for a few minutes, so as to thicken ; then take a piece of cloth and cover the pot, to put out the flame, and it will then be like syrup or thin tar.

This done, strain it through a silk stocking or handkerchief into a bottle and keep it closely corked. When you wish to use it, thin it with turpentine, but be careful and not use it too thin.

ANOTHER RECIPE.—Another good size for gilding may be made in this way : Procure some pure old drying oil, the older the better ; grind into it some ochre and a little of the best quality of red lead ; then thin it to a proper consistence ; form your letters carefully, laying it very even and thin, and let your work stand until so dry as only to have sufficient "tack" to hold your leaf. Apply the leaf with a gilder's tip carefully and lay it smooth with a flat camel-hair brush or a ball of fine cotton wool, but do not brush off all the superfluous gold until you are sure that the under size is perfectly dry and hard. This gives the gold its full brilliancy and stands the weather well.

QUICK DRYING SIZE.—Take a little good, quick-drying copal varnish ; add to it a small quantity of your old boiled drying oil, just enough to give it "tack," and when dry enough lay your leaf as before directed in page 29.

A SIZE KNOWN TO BUT FEW.—Take one pound of good, pure drying oil ; put it in a metal pot with a cover ; slowly add to this, after it has come almost to a boiling point, four ounces of pure gum animi (not copal ; gum dealers are of the opinion generally that animi and copal are one and the same, but such is not the case). Have your animi reduced to a fine powder ; take it upon the point of your pallet-knife and put it in cautiously, little by little, until you have it all in, allowing time to dissolve, and all the while keep stirring the mixture. Boil to the consistency of tar, and while warm strain it through a piece of silk into a heated, wide-mouthed bottle ; keep well corked, and when required, thin with turpentine and mix thoroughly. If you grind a little vermilion with this size it will show you what you are doing when using it.

This size will gild on glass, china, metal, signs, and nearly everything, and if properly made has no equal ; being more durable, it gives more luster to the gold than any other size, and has the very singular property of retaining the "tack" longer than any size known.

This is the "secret size," used by the best artists in London and Paris, and the one used by the justly celebrated japanners of Birmingham, who produce the finest work in decoration to be found in the world's market.

The artist must be furnished with a gilder's cushion, with parchment back and ends ; a knife to cut his gold ; a "tip," or brush, to lift his leaf with ; a ball of cotton wool, and a flat camel-hair brush to clean off with.

Take a little clean tallow on the back of the left hand, and then draw the "tip" quietly over the tallow and it will receive enough to take up the gold. Then place it lightly upon the work, to which it will adhere readily, and so continue until all your sized work has been covered with it.

The next thing to do is to pad it down lightly with your cotton ball, being careful to omit no portion of it, for if a mistake occurs on the first going over, you will find it very difficult to mend it afterward. So be particular in your work and miss no part of it. As before stated, do not thoroughly brush off your work until entirely dry.

Always, when gilding, try your size upon a piece of painted board or glass, in order to determine accurately the length of time it requires to dry. If it dries too quick, add some oil. If you size to day and gild to-morrow, and should you find the size too dry in the morning, you will have to add a little old, fat, raw linseed oil, as this tempers it so that you can set your own time for the gilding. A few experiments in this connection will enable you to master and regulate the nature and operation of size.

FOR A SIZE EXPOSED TO THE WEATHER.—One thing has been proved by experience, that is, that no gilding exposed to the extremes of summer and winter, wet and dry, cloud and sunshine, *should ever be varnished.*

The bare gold, if good, and on good size, will stand better, change less, retain its luster longer, with less liability to "dulce," or crack, than when varnished, although done with the best copal varnish ever made.

I have seen a sign done with gold, upon a black ground, that had stood the weather *forty years!* The board had given way to the effects of the weather, and had fallen away in many places, leaving the letters standing out bold, in good form and well preserved. So much for good size and *no* varnish.

GILDING ON GLASS FOR SIGNS.

This beautiful art is worked in many different ways, every artist having his own peculiar method.

One very good way is to first outline with a piece of hard soap your letters, scrolls, etc., (on the outside) then commence to outline on the glass (inside) with some suitable color, a light shade line for the top and left side of the letter ; then upon the bottom and right side of them use a black, or, in fact, almost any color you may select. When dry proceed to lay on your gold.

Some use gin, some whisky, others simply water ; gum arabic in solution, or white of egg, may be used. One can merely breathe upon the glass and it will sometimes answer the purpose of a "tack" for the gold.

I have found an excellent size, made from a solution of gum tragacanth in water. The first part that dissolves is the part that suits best ; that portion being pure, while the residue is cloudy and unfit for use.

When wanted to use, reduce a portion of the gum with water to a very weak standard, as in all cases you will find your gilding bright in exact ratio to the thinness and transparency of your size. I consider this the most desirable size, especially for large work.

NOTE.—For the instruction on *Gilding for Signs*, and the other information given from page 28 to 33 inclusive, credit is due to "Haney's Manual of Sign, Carriage, and Decorative Painting." In our present work we aim to give full information on Gilding in all its branches, and all necessary instruction on matters directly relating thereto. A multitude of valuable and interesting matters, which every sign, carriage and ornamental painter should be in possession of, do not come appropriately within the scope or capacity of this book, and we recommend all interested in those branches to refer to the "Manual of Sign, Carriage and Decorative Painting" for a full and practical course of instruction in those branches. The articles on Gilding which we quote are a sufficient evidence of the familiarity of the author with the subjects which he treats.

OUTLINING UPON GLASS.

First Method.—Draw your lines upon the glass at the proper distances for the size of your letters, etc., with a piece of hard soap, which will make very distinct lines. Then form your letters accurately, and in true distances or space, one from the other, being satisfied that all your proportions, etc., are correct. You will now be ready to commence your gilding.

Second Method.—Have your letters, etc., drawn out on fine paper ; prick with a pin the outlines of your letters, scrolls, etc Next take a bag made of muslin, filled with fine powdered charcoal ; lay the paper carefully to its proper place ; then pounce the charcoal bag against the paper, and you can then trace the outlines in full with black japan. To make all secure it will be necessary to give the work two or three coats, and when dry, wash or rub off all superfluities with a sponge or soft cotton rag.

N. B.—This method is only used after gilding, where the leaf is placed full without any outline.

Third Method.—To get accurate lines upon glass, preparatory to gilding. In the first place, clean the glass thoroughly ; then with a mixture of whiting, water, and a little milk, brush carefully all over the outside of the glass. When dry, draw your parallel lines, letters, scrolls, etc., with a pointed stick.

For small work, turn the glass around, and letter backward. If inside of a window, work upon the same principle. This is an easy and a true method of forming your lettering or ornamentation, as any fault in the drawing can be easily corrected.

Fourth Method.—In this plan it is necessary that the glass should be perfectly accessible on both sides—say for instance a glass door. The painter begins by painting the letters just as he wishes to have them—(unless he wishes to give them a shade in color, in which case he outlines the shadow) with a mixture of gum water and drop black on the front of the glass. Then going to the other side, or back of the door, he gilds as hereafter described. This obviates all difficulty about writing letters backward—as he has only to follow the lines he sees through the gold. Of course, in shaded letters, he only fastens the gilding over the body of the letter with black japan, and when the gold is rubbed off, he adds the shades. This method seems, in description, to take longer time than either of the others—but it really takes less.

MODUS OPERANDI FOR GILDING ON GLASS.

Whichever size you agree upon, lay it on with a full pencil, and proceed with your gold at once, so as to secure a solid "cover" without being obliged to "touch up," and if you wish to use two coats of gold, blow your breath upon the first coat to hold the second.

Lay as much gold as possible before your size dries, and so proceed until your lines are finished. Then rub it down gently to remove the superfluous gold. Then proceed to outline as in second method given ; or draw your parallel lines through the gilding (if in capitals of one given length) and cut in your letters with black japan very carefully, forming them all backward. This is the principle of the first method, but it requires considerable practice to do it correctly.

If any ornament is wanted in the body of the letters, lay them in with oil size. When dry, gild and shade if required. When all is dry, lay in the entire letter with the size (spirit or water size) and gild and back, as above, viz : with two or three coats of black japan.

The shading is done afterward, and in any colors the artist may decide upon. It generally takes two coats to cover solid upon glass. Gilding upon glass requires great practice and nice handling, but with proper care, this process looks very beautiful and stands well.

Silver leaf is laid on in the same manner, only it requires a little stronger size than the gold calls for. The silver being heavier relatively, use the size of gum tragacanth.

One point seems rather difficult—that of having to form the letters backward, but practice is the only thing that will make perfect in this respect, and enough of it will make, what at first seems a difficulty, as easy as the formation of letters in the ordinary way.

JAPANNED TIN SIGNS.

Draw your letters on paper to suit your sheet of tin, having first cleaned it with diluted alcohol and a piece of cotton. This will remove any grease or other matter that might hold the gold. Then take some whiting and rub it over the back of the paper upon which your design is made and lay it upon the japanned tin.

Place a weight upon the four corners of the paper, or otherwise fix it securely to the tin; then with a fine pointed piece of hard wood, trace the design carefully, bearing upon the paper with the point just hard enough to cause the whiting on the under side of the paper to adhere to the tin, and after going carefully over the whole, you will have transferred the entire design in fine white outlines to the tin you are to finish it upon.

Then paint your letters with either quick or slow drying *oil* size, and, when sufficiently dry for gilding, lay on the gold leaf, and "bat" it down thoroughly, afterward brushing off with your flat camel-hair brush or cotton.

GILDING ON MUSLIN OR SILK FOR PAINTERS.

For Masonic or Oddfellow's aprons, banners, or any work of like nature, a few words may be useful.

First have your material put upon a stretcher, and then complete your lettering and design. Prepare a size as follows: Dissolve bleached shellac in alcohol, and thin as much as will cover the parts to be painted or gilded, using the precaution to cut over the outline a little, so as to prevent the color from spreading.

Another size may be prepared by simply using the white of an egg. This size will do where the work is not exposed to the weather, or when it is required to be done quickly; and for such work, where gilding is to be done, lay the gold while the size is wet, and when dry, dust off the surplus gold and proceed with the painting, shading etc., when you are sure that the size is dry, remember.

SIZE FOR BRONZING AND GILDING.

A good size for bronzing, or pale gilding, is a mixture of asphaltum, drying oil, and spirits of turpentine.

A size for gilding on cloth, silk, plaster, etc., is made as follows: Take a little honey, combined with thick glue. When reduced properly, this size has the effect of brightening the color of the gold leaf, sticking to it well and giving it a very fine luster.

BURNISHED GILDING ON GLASS—LONDON METHOD.

The gold used is the ordinary gold leaf. Procure some fine isinglass, and place about as much in a tea-cup as will cover a sixpenny piece, and then pour on it about half a cupful of boiling water, which will dissolve the isinglass. Before the water is cold add about as much spirits of wine as there is water in the cup; then strain the whole through a clean silk handkerchief, and the mordant is ready for use. The addition of the spirits of wine is most material, as without it the gilding cannot be satisfactorily accomplished. Whatever may be the design or lettering to be executed on the glass, it must first be set out on a sheet of white paper, and painted with Brunswick black, so that it can be seen through the paper. This paper should be fixed at the edges or corners to front of the glass, the writing, of course appearing backward through the glass when looked at from the side to be gilded.

The glass having been thoroughly cleansed and rubbed with a silk handkerchief, the gilding may be commenced, the gold leaf being laid on the reverse side to that to which the paper is attached. It is usual to place the glass in a slanting position on an easel, the lines of lettering not being horizontal, or reading from left to right, but perpendicular, reading from top to bottom. The size is put on with a large soft camel-hair pencil, and the gold leaf applied in the usual way. If the line of writing is less than three inches in hight, it is advisable to gild the whole line, without paying any regard to the shapes of the letters, so that when the line is finished it will be a solid piece of gilding about the same hight and length as the letters. The first piece of gold leaf should be placed at the beginning of the line, which is the top of the glass, and each succeeding piece below it, the different pieces just overlapping each other. It is necessary to be particular in this, for if the pieces of gold do not meet, the interstices will probably show when the work is completed, and will prevent the uniformity of burnish.

For letters larger than three inches in hight, the gilding may be made to cover each letter. leaving the spaces between untouched. As soon as this part of the gilding has been completed it should be left to dry in a warm room, or placed before the fire, in which case it will be dry in a few minutes. When the gilding is perfectly dry and bright, it should be rubbed over very gently with a piece of cotton-wool. This will highten the burnish of the gold, and, and, remove the loose pieces which do not adhere to the glass.

After the gilding has been treated as described, a flat soft camel-hair brush charged with the isinglass size should be passed lightly over the work ; but not worked to and fro, or it will remove the gold leaf. The size should be flowed on freely and rapidly, and if any small pieces have been omitted, no attempt should be made to retouch them while the size is wet. When it is dry the gilding will resume its brightness. In order to complete the burnish of the gold, sometimes hot water is poured over the gilding, and this not only washes out any little specks which may appear on the front of the gold, but enhances its brilliancy considerably. The hotter the water poured over the work, the brighter does the gilding become, but care must be taken, as beyond certain degrees of heat the water will break the glass. This was very common, but the hot water bath now is often dispensed with, and the size coated over the gilding is applied hot. Another plan is to hold a hot flat iron near the work for a moment. This method is not quite so effective but it is much safer. The whole of the gilding has now to be repeated. A second layer of gold leaf over the first is necessary to ensure a satisfactory result. The second coat of gold is put on with the isinglass size, the same as the first ; and as it dries, the gilding viewed from the front of the glass will present a rich and finished appearance.

The loose pieces of gold should be removed as after the first coat, by means of cotton-wool gently rubbed over the work. Another coat of size made hot may now be applied, and the gilding is ready to be written upon. It is better to leave the gilding on for a day before writing upon it, because the isinglass does not get thoroughly hard, though to all appearance it is perfectly dry in an hour or two.

If the gilding is left untouched for two or three months, the action of the spirits of wine will cause the gold leaf to adhere so firmly to the glass that it will be difficult to remove it by any amount of washing with water ; whereas in the course of a few days after it is laid on, it may be readily removed by a damp sponge. The outline is transferred and the letters painted with Japan black and other methods.

When the japan is dry, the edges of the letters may be cut sharp and true by passing a small chisel along a straight edge, so as to trim the writing and make the tops and bottoms perfectly regular. All the straight lines of the letters may be thus trimmed, but the curved ones must be perfected with a writing pencil The softened colored thicknesses added to the letters are painted with the ordinary oil colors thinned with boiled oil and turpentine, the latter being used sparingly. Three or more tints are generally mixed on the palette, with a separate pencil to each, and these are softened with a larger sable pencil, and the outer edges are cut up with a pointed stick guided by a straight-edge, whilst the color is wet, and the superfluous color is wiped off with a piece of rag. By this means a sharpness of outline is obtained which the most skillful writer would fail to get by the mere use of the pencil. The shadow is put on as soon as the thickness is dry, and not being softened down, quick drying colors may be employed.

GILDER'S TOOLS.

The tools used by the gilder are few, and not very costly. A short description of each may be acceptable.

The *gilder's cushion* is used to spread the gold on, ready to cut

FIG. 1.—THE GILDER'S CUSHION.

up for use. It is a piece of wood about 8 inches by 5, covered with calf skin, with a piece of soft fabric introduced between the wood and the leather. The leather is strained tightly over the board, and nailed on to the edge. A piece of parchment about three or four inches broad is nailed half way round the board,

FIG. 2.—THE GILDER'S KNIFE.

and is meant to keep the gold leaf from flying off, as the least disturbance of the atmosphere is enough to send the gold leaf flying. A loop is placed under the cushion in which the thumb is inserted, and serves to carry the cushion. (See fig. 1.)

The *gilder's knife* is a light flexible blade, free from notches, but not very sharp, used to cut the gold on the cushion to the required shape. It must be kept clean, smooth in the edge, and bright, or it will tear instead of cut the gold. (See fig. 2.)

The *gilding "tip"* is a thin layer of flexible hair held together between two pieces of cardboard, and made of various widths,

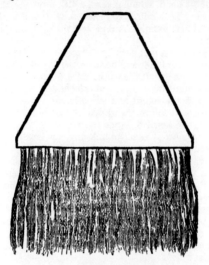

FIG. 3.—THE GILDING TIP.

and the length of hair varies also. The tip is used to convey the gold from the cushion to the work required to be gilded. The manner of using the cushion, the knife, and the tip, is as follows: The gilder first proceeds to open the book of gold leaf, and dexterously blows the leaf from the book into the cushion until he has about a dozen ready for use. He then takes up the cushion,

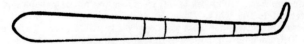

FIG. 4.—THE BURNISHER.

and slips his left hand thumb through the loop underneath; then with the end of the knife he carefully takes up a leaf of gold, and dexterously brings the metal to the front of the cushion, when with a slight puff of wind from the mouth on to the center of the leaf it is made to be perfectly flat. He then with the knife cuts it to the required shape, and places the knife between the fingers of the hand carrying the cushion. The tip (which is also carried between the fingers of the left hand) with the right hand is then drawn quickly across the hair of the workman's head, or across the back of his hand, which gives it a little moisture, and on being placed on the gold required to be lifted, carries it to the work to be gilded. This operation is repeated till the work is complete. (See fig. 3.)

The *burnisher* is a tool used by the gilder, and is made of either agate or flint. For beads and hollows, the burnishers are of differ-ent form and size to suit the work, and are usually curved near the end. The method of using the burnisher can only be attained by practice, when the sound and smooth passage of the burnisher over the gold will tell the workman if he has been successful in obtaining a good burnish. (See fig. 4.)

Brushes of various descriptions are constantly in use by the gilder ; ground hog's hair, flat and round; these are used for the various preparations of gold size: skewing brushes in quill are used for skewing or dabbing in the gold after it has adhered to the oil gold size: gilder's mops in quill are used to dab the gold to make it closely adhere to the size; camel's hair brushes of all sizes are useful, as well as sable and other tools.

Modelers, both steel and wood, are used to fashion ornaments that are broken and lost.

The gilder also uses pumice stones of various shapes, glass-paper, pallet knives, etc.

LAYING GOLD LEAF.

Some find it difficult to use the tip and cushion, owing to un-steadiness or want of "knack." All such might try the follow-ing method: Cut off the back of the book with a keen knife; have a flat dish with a little turpentine in it; take a small sponge, dampen with the turpentine and pass over the top of the book, so as to dampen the paper all over. The leaf will adhere as you lift the top sheet, which can be cut with scissors into any shape and carried to the work. This has been found an economical and also a quick way for most work, especially stripes. If carefully lifted, the gold will adhere to the paper without the use of turpen-tine.

GLASSWARE AND PORCELAIN.

TO GILD GLASSWARE AND PORCELAIN.

Drinking and other glasses are sometimes gilt on their edges. This is done either by using an adhesive varnish or by heat. The varnish is prepared by dissolving in boiled linseed oil an equal weight either of copal or amber. This is diluted by a proper quantity of oil of turpentine, so as to be applied as thin as possible to the parts of the glass intended to be gilt. When this is dry, which will be in about 24 hours, the glass is to be placed in a stove, till it is so warm as almost to burn the fingers when handled. At this temperature the varnish will become adhesive, and a piece of leaf gold, applied in the usual way, will immediately stick. Sweep off the superfluous portions of the leaf, and when quite cold it may be burnished, taking care to interpose a piece of very thin India paper between the gold and the burnisher. If the varnish is very good, this is the best method of gilding glass, as the gold is thus fixed on more evenly than in any other way.

PERMANENT GILDING BY HEAT.

It often happens with glassware or porcelain, when the varnish is but indifferent, that by repeated washing the gold wears off; on this account the practice of burning it in is sometimes had recourse to. For this purpose, some gold powder is ground with borax, and in this state applied to the clean surface of the glass by a camel-hair pencil; when quite dry, the glass is put into a stove heated to about the temperature of an annealing oven; the gum burns off, and the borax, by vitrifying, cements the gold with great firmness to the glass; after which it may be burnished. The gilding upon porcelain is in like manner fixed by heat and the use of borax.

GILDING ON PORCELAIN OR GLASS BY DIPPING.

Mix first in a glass mortar, and then between a muller and a ground plate glass, neutral chloride of platinum with rectified essence of lavender, so as to form a thin syrup, which is applied with a brush in very thin layers upon the glass, porcelain, or other ceramic object. After drying, heat in a muffle up to a dark red; this temperature reduces the platinum to the metallic state; it then appears with a perfect polish. After cooling, pass the whole object through aquafortis, which is without action upon the platinum, but destroys the impurities which may tarnish its surface. Rinse in plenty of water, wrap the object with a few turns of fine brass wire, having numerous points of contact with the platinized places, and dip into the gold bath. After a few minutes the platinum is covered with gold which has the same adherence and polish. Rub the gold with chamois leather; this method dispenses with burnishing, which is costly, and often impracticable in the deeply indented parts. If the gilding is too red, add to the bath a few drops of a solution of double cyanide of potassium and silver liquor for silver electroplating. This method is preferable to that of baths with separate battery; the gilding has a bright instead of a dead luster, and its adherence is greater.

Another Method.—The following is said to give good results: Pure chloride of gold is dissolved in water, so that each quart of water shall carry in solution after careful filtering three quarters of a grain of gold. Neutralize the solution with soda. A portion of alcohol is then mixed with an equal quantity of water and a stream of hydrogen gas driven through it until it will receive no more gas. The glass being then perfectly cleaned and a border put around it of wax, or other material one-tenth of an inch thick, a portion of alcohol and water is mixed with sufficient chloride to cover the glass. Precipitation is said to commence in a few minutes, the gold coming out quite bright, and making a tolerably firm coating.

GILDING ON METALS.

GILDING ON METALS BY DIPPING.

The baths employed contain gold in the form of a double salt of protoxide, and should possess little stability, that is to say, be decomposed and abandon the gold under feeble influences, and should dissolve the copper placed in them in equivalent proportion to that of the deposited gold, thus forming a new double salt in which the copper is in the same degree of oxidation as the gold. When the articles have been previously amalgamated, it is mercury and not copper which is substituted for gold in the solution.

Distilled water, seventeen pints; pyrophospate of potash, of soda, twenty-eight ounces; hydrocyanic acid of twelve and a half per cent. strength prussic acid, one-third of an ounce; crystalized perchloride of gold, two-thirds of an ounce. The pyrophosphate of soda is most generally employed, and is obtained by melting, at a white heat, the ordinary crystalized phosphate of soda. The pyrophosphate of soda may be obtained in the form of crystals, which is a proof of a definite composition. The quantity of chloride represents a little more than one-third of an ounce of pure gold treated by aqua regia. Put 16 pints of distilled water in a porcelain vessel, or an enameled cast-iron kettle, and add, by small portions at a time, and stirring with a glass rod, the pyrophosphate; heat, filter and let it cool down. The chloride of gold is prepared by introducing into a small glass flask pure gold finely laminated, of one-third of an ounce; hydrochloric acid, pure, nearly one ounce; nitric acid, pure, one-half an ounce. The flask is slightly heated, effervescence and abundant nitrous vapors result, and in a few minutes the gold has entirely disappeared, leaving a reddish-yellow liquor. The flask is then put upon a sheet of iron, with a hole in its center, and supported by a tripod. The whole is heated by a gas or spirit lamp to evaporate excess of the acids; too much acidity may cause great irregularities in the working of the bath, and even prevent its action altogether. An excess of nitric acid causes a jumping of the heated liquors, and may overthrow the whole; it is preferable to have the hydrochloric acid predominating. The evaporation is finished when vapors escape slowly from the flask, and when the liquid has become of an oily consistency and of a deep red color. The flask is then removed from the fire by wooden pincers, and set to cool upon a ring of plaited straw. If a more rapid evaporation is desired, heat the flask over ignited charcoal, or the spirit lamp; agitate the liquid to prevent any of the gold from returning to the metallic state. Well prepared chloride of gold, when cold, forms a saffron-yellow crystalline mass. If the color is red, it has been too much evaporated, and will do very well for electro-baths; but for dipping baths it must be heated again after a small addition of the two acids. If the perchloride of gold, by too protracted a heat, has passed to the state of insoluble **protochloride, of** even for metallic gold, the treatment

must be begun again with the indicated mixture of pure nitric
and hydrochloric acids. The perforated sheet of iron, upon
which the flask rests, is intended to prevent the action of heat
upon the sides of the vessel, which will decompose the films of
chloride of gold wetting the flask at these places. When the
chloride of gold is cold and crystallized, dissolve it in the flask
with a little distilled water, and pour the solution through a
paper filter held in a glass funnel into a clean bottle; this is to
separate a small quantity of silver always found in the gold of the
trade. Rinse the flask and filter with the unemployed water, so
as to get all the gold into the bath. Pour the filtered solution of
chloride of gold into the cooled one of pyroposphate, and stir
with a glass rod. Lastly, add the hydrocyanic acid, and the
bath is heated nearly to the boiling point for use. If the solution
of pyrophosphate is still tepid, add the hydrocyanic acid before
the chloride of gold. Hydrocyanic or prussic acid is not absolutely necessary; but, without it, the bath is too easily decomposed, and the gold is too rapidly precipitated upon the objects
placed in it. When the solutions are mixed in the cold, the
liquor is yellow or greenish-yellow; but becomes colorless by
the increase of temperature. If the liquor becomes currant-red,
or wine-lees violet, it is an indication that there is too little
hydrocyanic acid; add it drop by drop, until the liquor becomes
colorless. An excess of this acid is objectionable, but there is
a very simple method of keeping the baths in good working
order, by adding prussic acid gradually to those too rich in gold;
or correcting any excess of prussic acid with a small proportion
of chloride of gold, until the gilding is produced without difficulty and of the proper sh de. Thus prepared, the bath will
produce very fine gilding upon well-cleansed articles, which must
also have passed through a very diluted solution of nitrate of
binoxide of mercury, without which the deposit of gold is red
and irregular, and will not cover the soldered portions. The
articles are supported by a hook or in a stoneware ladle perforated with holes, or in brass gauze baskets; they must be constantly agitated whilst in the bath. Gilders usually employ three
baths, placed in close proximity to each other, and heated in the
same furnace; the first bath is one deprived of gold by a previous
operation, and is used for removing all excess of which may
remain upon the articles; the second bath still retains some gold,
but not enough to give a sufficiently rich gilding. The pieces
passed through it begin to receive the deposit, which will be
finished in thickness and shade in the third bath. A gas furnace,
easy to manage, and clean in its working, may be arranged by
having a properly supported sheet-iron plate, with holes cut out

where the kettles are to stand. Under each kettle place suitable gas burner; when the baths have been heated nearly up to boil ing point, lower the gas, so as not to increase the temperature. This method produces much more gilding with a given quantity of gold, than one bath alone. The gilding is done in a few seconds; the finishing operations consist in rinsing in fresh water, drying in dry and warm saw-dust, and burnishing, if desired.

COLORING PROCESS.

If the gilding is dull and irregular in color, melt together in their water of crystallization, at about 212° Fahr., equal parts of sulphate of iron, sulphate of zinc, sulphate of alumina and potash and saltpeter. Cover the articles with the mixture, and put them into a cylindrical and vertical grate. This is placed in the center of a furnace, where the charcoal burns between the sides and the grate which holds the articles. When the moistened finger is presented to one piece, and a slight hissing sound is heard, the heat has been sufficiently raised; put all the articles rapidly into a very diluted solution of sulphuric acid, where the coating of salts is quickly dissolved; the articles present a warm, uniform shade of color. If the copper articles are not entirely gilt by the first operation, the ungilt portions will show themselves by a red coloration, and the articles must then be deprived of gold, cleansed, and gilt anew. Sometimes, when the first gilding is imperfect, instead of coloring by the process just described, the articles are placed for a few moments into the electro-bath.

For articles which require a good plating there is an easy method by this process of obtaining as good results as by the battery; it consists in gilding several times, by dipping; before each dipping, the article is passed through the solution of nitrate of binoxide of mercury. Gilding by dipping is superior to that by electricity in depth of shade, brightness, and especially in not scaling off, as the deposit is of pure gold only.

ORMOLU COLORING.

This operation consists in smearing, by means of a brush, the gilt and scratch-brushed objects with a thin paste of nitrate of potash, alum, and oxide of iron, which have been well mixed and ground under the muller, and to which has been added a solution of saffron, annatto, or any coloring substance according to the shade desired. If the gilding is strong and thick, the objects are then heated until this coating curls over at the approach of a wet finger. If the gilding is a mere film, the mixture is simply allowed to stand upon the articles for a few minutes. In either case, the whole is rapidly washed in warm water holding in suspension a certian quantity of the materials for ormolu ; they are then rapidly dried, when they appear of a darker shade ; remove any portions too much colored by striking them vertically with a brush having long bristles. If the tint does not appear satisfactory, commence the operation afresh, after washing off the ormolu in a diluted solution of sulphuric acid.

GREEN AND WHITE GILDING.

These shades may be graduated at will, and are obtained by adding, drop by drop, until the desired shade is arrived at, to the bath of double pyrophosphate of soda and gold, a solution of nitrate of silver. For the solution of nitrate of silver, dissolve in 5 oz. of distilled water, $\frac{1}{2}$ oz. of nitrate of silver crystallized, or of lunar caustic. Before gilding green or white, yellow gild the objects in the ordinary bath, then pass them rapidly through the mercurial solution, and, lastly, dip them into the gold bath holding the nitrate of silver, which parts rapidly with its silver upon the first articles steeped in it. It is necessary to maintain the constancy of the shade by the addition of a few drops of the silver solution when required.

GILDING SILVER BY DIPPING.

The silver articles, previously cleansed and scratch-brushed, are boiled for about half an hour in the gold bath of pyrophosphate, to which add a few drops of sulphurous acid, or, preferably, hydrocyanic acid, in excess of the quantity needed by the primitive bath. This gilding is very fine, but without firmness. The deposit is rendered more rapid and thicker when the silver articles are stirred with a rod of copper, zinc, or brass.

GOLD DIPPING BATH WITH BICARBONATES.

The bicarbonate bath is prepared in a cast-iron kettle, turned clean and smooth inside on the lathe, and gilt by the protracted ebullition of nearly spent gold baths. Water, $3\frac{1}{2}$ galls. ; bicarbonate of potash of soda, $\frac{1}{3}$ oz. ; pure metallic gold, transformed into chloride, $4\frac{1}{4}$ oz. The whole is boiled for at least two hours, and fresh water added to replace that evaporated. A part of the gold in the form of a violet-black powder, precipitates, and requires the cooling and decanting of the liquor. This is boiled again and the gilding proceeded with in the same manner as before described except that the mercurial solution should be more diluted than for the baths of pyrophosphates. The operation is finished when about half of the gold in the liquor is deposited. The remainder goes to the saved waste. The bicarbonate process is inferior in most respects to the pyrophosphate, and it is now rarely used.

GILDING BY DILUTED BATH.

This bath should be employed only as a complement to the cleansing process, before a more resisting gilding, as its results have little durability. Water, 2 galls. ; bicarbonate of potash, 7 oz. ; caustic potash, 63 oz. ; cyanide of potassium, 3 oz. ; metallic gold to be transformed into chloride, $\frac{1}{4}$ oz. The whole is brought up to the boiling point, and a pale gilding is obtained even upon articles imperfectly cleansed, and without using nitrate of binoxide of mercury. It is possible to add $\frac{1}{4}$ oz. of chloride of gold several times to this bath without any other substances. Afterward maintain it at the proper strength by additions of gold and salts in the above proportions, and it will last for an indefinite period. This bath will gild about 140 oz. of small jewelry with $\frac{1}{30}$ oz. of gold, whereas a pyrophosphate bath gilds only about 35 oz. of small articles with the $\frac{1}{30}$ oz. of gold extracted from the liquor.

GILDING SMALL METAL ARTICLES BY STIRRING AND GOLD AMALGAM.

In the center of a charcoal stove put a crucible holding a given quantity of pure and dry mercury, and when the temperature has reached about 212 Fahr. add one-half the weight of gold. Stir with an iron rod until the amalgam has acquired the consistence of butter, throw it into cold water, and keep it there for use.

Cleanse the articles to be gilded in aquafortis, put them in a stoneware pan, and pour over them a diluted solution of nitrate of binoxide of mercury, taking care to move the articles about all the time, in order to cover them with a regular white coating of mercury. Add the desired proportion of amalgam ; on stirring the articles this is spread all over them.

Then rinse the articles in cold water, place them in a large and deep copper ladle, perforated with numerous small holes, and having a long handle. Hold the ladle over a charcoal fire, and constantly stir it about in order to have the heat equal everywhere. The mercury of the amalgam is soon volatilized, and the gold remains adherent to the articles.

If instead of a yellow gilding a red one is desired, this is got by waxing, which consists in pouring upon the pieces, kept in the ladle and upon the fire, in a well mixed and fluid state : oil, 25 parts ; yellow wax, 25 ; acetate of copper, 10 ; red ochre, 40. The articles must be constantly agitated, and the mixture allowed to burn out, when the whole is thrown into a very diluted solution of sulphuric acid. The waxing is only to be done after the comple volatilization of the mercury.

When removed from the pickle, the gilding has the dull ochre appearance, and must be scratch-brushed. Small articles are brightened in a long narrow bag, where they are put with copper pearls, or the waste from these pearls, and wet with vinegar water ; a to-and-fro motion is imparted to the bag, and the gilt articles and the copper granules polish each other. Rinse and dry in saw-dust, and burnish if required. Five grains of gold are enough to well gild a gross of old-fashioned buttons.

GILDING BY FIRE OR MERCURY.

Mercury gilding will furnish gold with a bright or a dead luster, scratch-brushed, ormolued, and with different shades. The amalgam of gold is prepared in the manner described in the process of gilding by stirring, only a little less mercury is used, in order to have an amalgam about as hard as wax. This amalgam is crystalline, and a certain crackling sound is heard when the crystals are crushed between the fingers. A stock of amalgam is generally prepared in advance, and is divided into small balls of nearly equal size, the value of which is ascertained from their number, and from the total weight of gold employed. These balls are kept in water, but should not remain too long without being used, as the different parts do not then present the same composition. The amalgam is spread with the finger upon a flat, hard stone called the gilding stone ; and having dipped a scratch-brush of stout brass wire into a solution of nitrate of binoxide of mercury until it becomes completely white, it is passed over the amalgam, a portion of which is carried away. The object, previously well cleansed, is scratch-brushed in every direction, and the brush must be frequently dipped into the mercurial solution to facilitate the regular and even spreading of the amalgam. This operation requires great care to obtain a uniform coat upon the hollow and raised parts.

When the back part of a piece does not require gilding, the flat outline, and the back edge, should be gilt, so that the naked copper shall cause no injury in the subsequent operations. The ar-

ticle, when uniformly covered with the amalgam, is heated upon
a charcoal fire without draught, which rests upon a cast-iron
plate. It is advisable to employ a gilding forge, which allows
the workman to watch the operation from behind a glass frame,
which protects him from the mercurial vapors. The entire attention is now required for watching the process. With the left
hand covered with a thick glove of buckskin, turn the piece in
every direction upon the fire. and, as the mercury disappears,
with the right hand strike the article in every direction with a
brush, the handle and the bristles of which must be long, to equal-
ize the gilding, and to push the remaining amalgam upon those
parts which appear less charged with it. When all the mercury
has volatilized, the gilding has a dull, greenish-yellow color, re-
sembling that of boxwood ; examine whether the coat of gold is
continuous. Should a few empty places appear, add more amalgam, and heat the whole again.

The next operation is scratch-brushing; which furnishes a pale
green color, and requires another heating for arriving at the desired shade. The reheating should expel any remaining mercury,
and produce a fine orange-yellow color. In case a bright luster
is required, submit the object, with the aid of heat, to the ormolu
process already described. To obtain dead luster, the object is
firmly fixed to an iron rod, by wire of the same metal, and
smeared with a hot paste for dead gilding, composed of saltpeter,
common salt, and the double sulphate of alumina and potash.
The whole is heated upon a brisk charcoal fire, without draught,
and moved about until the mixture dries and begins to fuse,
when the article is immediately placed in a barrel half filled with
water. The covering of salts dissolves, and the dead luster appears ; this operation requires a certain amount of practice.
The gilding must be strong to stand the dead luster process, especially when the first trial is not successful. The red lines left
by the iron wire disappear by plunging the object into a not too
diluted solution of nitric acid, or pure hydrochloric acid. Mercury gilders do not employ pure gold ; what they use is previously alloyed with a certain portion of copper or silver. With
the latter metal the gilding is green. Red gilding is either obtained with a dark ormolu or with the green for red, already mentioned.

COLD GILDING WITH THE RAG.

Dissolve finely laminated pure gold in aqua regia made of nitric
acid, 10 parts ; sal ammoniac, 4 ; saltpeter, 1. Heat carefully
upon a gentle fire ; when all the gold has disappeared, pour the
cooled contents of the flask into a flat-bottomed stoneware pan.

Into this liquor, place one upon the other, and in sufficient quantity, squares of linen cloth, stir them with a glass rod, in order that they may absorb the chloride of gold. Each square of cloth is taken out with wooden pincers, well drained, and spread for drying in a dark chamber.

When nearly dry, each piece of cloth, supported upon glass rods, is placed on top of a charcoal fire, and soon takes fire. The combustion is aided by the presence of the saltpeter, and is finished upon a marble slab. Grind the ashes under a muller, collect and keep them between the folds of a parchment leaf, around which a wet cloth has been folded. The powder is then ready to use ; mix it upon a slab with a few drops of water, and with this paste rub the well cleaned surfaces of the silver to be gilt.

The smooth surfaces are rubbed with the thumb, the fillets or grooves with a fine cork cut to the proper shape, and the corners or angles with a stick of soft wood, such as linden or poplar ; the articles are then burnished. This gilding is very thin, but quite resisting, especially after the action of the burnishing tool, which forces the gold into the pores of the silver.

If a red shade be desired, add a small proportion of pure copper to the gold to be dissolved in aqua regia.

GRECIAN GILDING FOR BRASS AND COPPER ONLY.

Equal parts of sal-ammoniac and corrosive sublimate are dissolved in nitric acid and a solution of gold made with this menstruum. The silver brushed over with it turns black, but on exposure to a red heat it assumes the color of gold.

GILDING BY DIPPING ON SMALL SCALE.

Take one-half ounce of nitric and one-half ounce muriatic acid ; dissolve in these one pennyweight of gold, gently evaporate until it crystallizes, then add two ounces of cyanide of potassium dissolved in fifteen ounces of water. The article to be gilded is to be simply put in the solution, and a piece of *clean* zinc placed on it, and moved from one spot to another until it is sufficiently covered with gold. The vessel containing the solution should be porcelain.

GILDING ON STEEL BY DIPPING.

In any quantity of nitro-muriatic acid (*aqua regia*) dissolve gold or platina, until, on the application of heat, no effervescence ensues. Evaporate the solution thus formed to dryness by means of a gentle heat ; then dissolve the dry mass thus formed in the least possible amount of water. Take the instrument known by chemists as a separating funnel, which may contain a liquid

ounce ; a quarter fill it with the liquid, and the other three parts
fill with the best sulphuric ether. The two liquids should not
mix. Then holding the tube in a horizontal position, turn it
round with the finger and thumb. When the ether has become
impregnated with the gold or platina, which may be known by
its change of color, replace it in a perpendicular position, and
having stopped up the orifice with a cork, let it stand for twenty-
four hours. At the end of this time the liquid will be divided
into two parts, the darkest colored being below. Take out the
cork and let the dark liquid flow off, and stop the tube immediately with the cork. What remains in the tube is the gilding
liquid. *The article to be gilded* must be perfectly free from rust
or grease, and have received the highest possible polish. The
process of gilding is as follows : A vessel of glass or unglazed
ware having been procured, it should be filled nearly to the top
with the gilding liquid. The article should be dipped in this for
a moment, and then be plunged into clear water and well rinsed.
After having been thoroughly dried with blotting-paper, it
should be placed in a temperature of 150° Fahr. until it is heated
throughout, and then polished with rouge and wash-leather ; or,
better still, be burnished. Take care that the muriate of gold is
quite free from excess of acid, and be careful to follow exactly
the above directions in every particular, as only by doing so can
perfect success be ensured.

GILDING COPPER CHAINS, ETC., BY DIPPING.

Take a solution of nitro-muriate of gold (gold dissolved in a
mixture of aquafortis and muriatic acid), and add to a gill of it a
pint of ether or alcohol, then immerse your copper chain in it for
about fifteen minutes, when it will be coated with a film of gold.
The copper must be perfectly clean, and free from oxide, grease,
or dirt, or it will not take on the gold.

COPPER, BRASS, IRON OR STEEL WITH LEAF GOLD.

Heat the articles, after thorough cleaning from rust or grease,
to a blue shade ; apply the leaf and burnish down with a steel
burnisher. Add leaf upon leaf in the same manner, until the
gilding is as thick as desired. Iron or steel receive the gold better if dipped for a few moments in sulphate of copper solution,
so as to receive a *flash* of copper ; or into a bath of the nitrate of
the binoxide of mercury.

GILDING BY THE USE OF THE BATTERY.

BATTERIES.

For gilding and silvering there are used four different kinds of batteries. The Daniels, the Smee, the Bunsen, and the Watts batteries. We will describe the latter because it may be made by any one and fully answers the purpose.

The battery which I would recommend, says Mr. Alexander Watts, to the attention of the electro gilder, and those who desire to deposit metals by electricity on a moderate scale, consists of a

FIG. 5.—WATTS BATTERY.

cylindrical stone jar A (fig 5), capable of holding about four gal-lons ; inside this jar is fitted a cylinder of sheet copper c (this may be one sixty-fourth of an inch in thickness), a strip of the cop-per cylinder B, about half an inch broad, is cut off to within one inch, so as to form the positive electrode ; my motive in doing this is to insure a perfect connection between the positive pole and the cylinder, and to save the trouble of soldering.

A circular piece of wood forms a covering to the jar ; in the centre of this cover, a hole about two inches in diameter is bored, to which an ox-gullet or weazand, D, is fastened, extend-ing to the bottom of the jar, the lower end of which is carefully tied with a piece of thick twine ; or a porous cell may be used

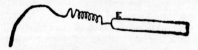

FIG. 6.—ZINC BAR.

instead if preferred. A zinc bar E (fig 2) is cast, with a long and tolerably thick copper wire in it, one end of which has been pre-

viously coiled into a helix, so as to form a spring, to prevent the
breaking off of the wire at its junction with the zinc bar. The
ox-gullet, or cell, is now nearly filled with a concentrated solution
of common salt, to which a few drops of hydrochloric acid have
been added, and the zinc bar immersed in it, but not allowed to
touch the bottom of the gullet, or cell, which it may be prevented
from doing by attaching a piece of wood across the zinc bar, to
suspend it from the cover of the battery. The jar is nearly filled
with water acidulated with two pounds of sulphuric acid and one
ounce of nitric acid, and the battery is ready for use. P and N
(fig 5) signifying positive and negative poles.

In the above form of battery several advantages present themselves ; its action is constant, there is but little local action, and
consequently but little waste ; its current is regular, and it is
very economical in its construction and inexpensive in use.

A compound battery thus constructed will give most powerful
effects when a number of cells are used, and it will continue to
give these effects for a greater length of time than any battery
with which I am acquainted.

In a single cell of this battery, a considerable quantity of electricity is disengaged, of sufficient intensity for small operations,
such as gilding and so forth. When it is desired to deposit a large
quantity of metal in a given time, several of these cells alternated,
that is, having the zinc wire of one cell united to the copper
cylinder of the next, and so on, may be employed, by which arrangement a vast amount of metal may be deposited in a short
time, when the solution is in good working condition. But it is
preferable to unite all the copper wires and the zinc wires, by
which arrangement the intensity is not increased.

The Daniells battery, is mainly used for electrotyping, obtaining
copies of casts, &c., as it works slowly and solidly. It consists
of a copper vessel any desired size. Within this stands the porous
cup, and within the cup a thick zinc plate or cylinder. The
negative wire proceeds from the zinc and the positive from the
copper vessel. Inside the porous cup there is poured strong salt
water—outside of it a solution of blue vitriol (sulphate of copper).
The fluid in the two vessels should stand about the same hight,
or if there is any difference that in the porous cup should stand
higher. This acts just as the previous battery ; the object to be
coppered being attached to the zinc wire, and the waste being
supplied by some crystals of sulphate of copper on a little shelf
in the copper vessel. In coppering small articles the work can be
perfectly done in the battery itself by suspending the object in the
sulphate solution—but in large works or in depositing other metals
use a separate bath for the solution, the connection being made

by brass rods laid over the bath and connected with the two wires. Care must, however, be taken by the operator to have all the connections clean, and the bath perfectly insulated.

The Smee battery consists of a glass or porcelain jar, a plate of silver covered with a film of platina (by dipping it into a solution of chloride of platina) fixed in a wooden clamp between two zinc plates—but not touching them—being kept separate by a band of gutta percha around the silver plate. To *one* of the zinc plates and to the silver plate are attached the usual thumb screws to hold the wires for connections—and the articles to be plated are placed in a separate bath suspended from the zinc wire—while the anode or metal plate to supply metal withdrawn from the solution by the process, is suspended from the wire proceeding from the silver plate. These batteries are made in all sizes—a battery of four two-quart batteries being sufficient for the ordinary work of jewelers. Sulphuric acid one part to sixteen water is the exciting fluid, and the zincs should be covered with quicksilver. This is done by first cleaning the zincs in a strong solution of sulphuric acid and water, and then rubbing well with quicksilver by means of a brush. The quicksilver should be contained in a dish. When the battery becomes inactive, the zincs must be cleaned and freshly rubbed with quicksilver.

The Bunsen battery consists of the usual glass or porcelain jar containing a porous cup containing a plate of coke or carbon, and a cylinder of zinc surrounding the porous cup, but not touching it. Within the porous cup is nitric acid undiluted, and outside of the cup is a solution of sulphuric acid one part, and water, nine parts. The wires proceed from the coke and zinc respectively. This battery works with great intensity, and is mainly used for plating iron and steel and Britannia metal, or in giving coats of brass, tin, platinum, etc. It is better to buy it than to make it, and all parts not intended to be acted on by the acids must be carefully protected by some acid-proof coating.

A simple form of battery is something like a Daniells reversed, and can be made with an ordinary copper cup or kettle.

Into a copper vessel is put a sheet of zinc bent into a cylinder, and surrounding a porous cup. The zinc must stand on glass or other non-conductor, and must touch neither copper nor cup. A copper wire may be soldered to it. This battery is excited by filling the porous cup with the gold solution, and the space outside of the cup with strong salt water. Have both fluids the same hight. Put a lighted lamp under the copper until the solution reaches a temperature of about 200 degrees—hang the articles to be plated from the wire (attached to the zinc) in the gold solution, and in a few minutes they will take a thin but beautiful *flash* of gold.

GOLD ELECTRO-GILDING BATHS.

Distilled water, 2¼ gallons ; cyanide of potassium, ordinary 70 per cent., 10½ oz. ; pure gold, 3½ oz. ; aqua ammonia, 17½ oz. Heat the gold in a glass flask with 9 oz. of pure hydrochloric acid, and 4½ oz. of pure nitric acid. When the gold is dissolved, continue the heat in order to expel the acid fumes, and until the color of the liquid is dark red, nearly black. Remove from the fire, and dissolve the crystalline mass formed in cooling in 3 or 4 pints of water, and pour into a large porcelain dish. Add the ammonia, which produces an abundant yellow precipitate of gold ammonium ; pour upon filtering paper, and the filtered liquid, which still contains traces of gold, is kept with the saved waste Wash the precipitate remaining upon the filter several times with cold water, until it no longer smells of ammonia. It must not be dried, as it is a fulminating mixture, and consequently very dangerous.

Next dissolve in the vessel used as a bath the cyanide of potassium in the distilled water. Filter, and add the wet gold ammonium, which rapidly dissolves when stirred, and forms a clear gold bath. But before using it cold, the ammonia should be expelled by boiling for about one hour.

For a newly-prepared cold electro-gilding bath, the ordinary cyanide of potassium is preferable, on account of the potash it contains, which renders the liquor a better conductor of electricity. But for the preservation of the strength, the pure cyanide is better, as it possesses the advantage of a constant composition, and does not load the solution with foreign salts.

The gold solution for maintaining the metallic strength of the bath is prepared as follows : Transform the gold into precipitate of gold ammonium, as above described, place it in water, 2 pints of water to 4 oz. gold, then add cyanide of potassium until the liquor is colorless. If there is not sufficient water with the gold ammonium, the liquor will be dark red, and will not be decolorized by cyanide.

ANOTHER GOLD ELECTRO-GILDING BATH.

Distilled water, 2¼ gallons ; cyanide of potassium, pure, 7 oz. ; or ordinary cyanide, according to strength, 10 to 14 oz. ; pure gold, 3½ oz. Make a neutral chloride of gold, as in the preceding formula, and, when cold and crystallized, dissolve it in 3½ pints of water. Filter if needed. Dissolve the cyanide in 14 pints of water, filter, and mix the two solutions, which become colorless When it is possible to boil this bath for half an hour before using it, it **becomes a better** conductor of electricity, and the gilding is more uniform. Its strength is maintained by additions of neutral chloride of gold and pure cyanide of potassium, from 1 to 1½ of pure cyanide to 1 of gold.

Both the above baths may be diluted with once or twice their volume of water; the gilding will remain fine, but the proportion of gold deposited will be less in a given length of time.

CHLORIDE OF GOLD ELECTRO-GILDING BATH.

Yellow prussiate of potash, 7 oz.; pure carbonate of potash, 5 oz.; sal ammoniac, 1 oz.; pure gold transformed into chloride, ½ oz.; water, 2½ gallons. Boil all the salts together, less the chloride of gold, separate by filtration the precipitate of carbonate of iron, then add the chloride of gold dissolved in a little water, and allow the bath to cool off. Any kind of gold salt, and the oxide, or even finely-powdered metal, may take the place of the chloride of gold; but the latter is preferred on account of the facility of its preparation, and of its solubility. Any kind of gold salt will be transformed into cyanide by the cyanide of potassium. The small proportion of the chloride of potassium resulting from the transformation of the chloride of gold into cyanide does not prevent the good working of the baths. The addition of a little prussic acid produces a brighter, but thinner, gilding. The indicated cyanides may be replaced by the cyanides of sodium, calcium, and ammonium.

GENERAL MANIPULATION.

Cold gilding baths are generally kept in porcelain or stoneware vessels; but for large volumes of liquor use wooden troughs lined with gutta-percha plates. The sides of the troughs support anodes of laminated gold, which dip entirely into the liquor, and are held by small platinum wires; they are connected with the positive pole of the battery. Suspend the articles by means of metallic slinging wires to a movable frame of clean brass rods connected with the negative pole.

The deposit of gold should be pure yellow, but it has sometimes a dull earthy gray color. In that case scratch-brush it with the greatest care, and then pass it through the ormolu coloring. The gold anode conducts the electricity, and also maintains the metallic strength of the bath up to a certain point; but it is necessary to add now and then either the oxide or the chloride of gold, and a certain proportion of cyanide of potassium, to make up for that transformed into carbonate of potash and cyanide of ammonia.

The proportion of cyanide is about double that of the chloride of gold added ; this is ascertained by the color of the bath and the shade of the deposit ; if the proportion of the chloride of gold is too great, add more cyanide. If gold predominates, the deposit is quite black or dark red ; when the cyanide is in excess, the gilding is very slow and gray, and it will sometimes happen that pieces already gilt will lose their gold.

When the bath is not in use, the gold anode must be removed from it, otherwise it will be dissolved. If the anode were partly immersed in the bath, it would be rapidly cut at the level of the liquid ; for this reason use the platinum wires, which are not acted upon. It is remarkable that the solution of cyanides, even without the action of the electric current, rapidly dissolve all the metals except platinum in the cold or at a moderate temperature, and that at the boiling point they have scarcely any action upon the metals.

Cold electro-gilding should be done slowly; and it is necessary to often look at the pieces in the bath, and scratch-brush those with an irregular deposit, or with dark spots. The intensity of the current should be often changed by increasing or diminishing the number of the elements, or the strength or the volume of the liquors in the battery.

With too much intensity in the current, the deposit is black or red ; it is yellow with the proper amount of electricity. With a weak current those portions opposite the anode only get covered with gold ; it is well to change the position of the objects often, in order that the deposit be regular.

With a freshly-prepared bath it may happen that surfaces already gilt will lose their gold by changing their positions. This is a sign that the bath contains too much cyanide of potassium, and too little gold, or that the electric current is too weak.

IMPROVING APPEARANCE AFTER COLD BATH.

When the deposit obtained in cold baths is unsatisfactory in appearance, although the quantity is sufficient, the proper shade may be imparted by—

1. The gilt article is steeped in a solution of nitrate of binoxide of mercury, until it has become white. It is heated afterward to volatilize the mercury, and scratch-brushed.

2. Place the article into concentrated sulphuric acid, then heat it until abundant white fumes are disengaged, throw it, still hot, into a weak pickle of sulphuric acid. In this case, the acid has destroyed the organic impurities which may exist in the deposit, and reduces the subsalts of gold to the metallic state.

3. Smear the article with a thick paste of water and powdered borax, or with biphosphate of lime of the consistency of honey, and heat until igneous fusion takes place. Then put the article into diluted sulphuric acid, which dissolves the borax or the biphosphate, and leaves the gold with its natural bright luster.

When, after scratch-brushing small gilt articles, their color is not entirely satisfactory, it may be improved by plunging the articles again into the bath but for an instant, and then immediately into boiling water. For gilding German silver, the solution should be worked at rather a low temperature, and with a less surface of anode. The solution should be just so weak in precious metal, that the German silver will not precipitate the gold without the aid of the battery; otherwise the deposit will take place so rapidly that the gold will peel off when being burnished or scratch-brushed.

GOLD ELECTRO-PLATING IN HOT BATHS.

Is more regular, more rapidly obtained, and possesses a deeper shade, than that by cold baths. 1. Crystallized phosphate of soda, 21 oz. ; bisulphite of soda, 3½ oz ; pure cyanide of potassium, ¼ oz.; pure gold, transformed into chloride, ⅓ oz.; distilled water, 2¼ gallons. This is satisfactory for electro-gilding silver, bronze, and other alloys rich in copper. For gilding wrought and cast iron and steel directly, without a previous coat of copper, the bath is modified as follows : Distilled water, 2¼ gallons; phosphate of soda, 17¼ oz.; bisulphate of soda, 4½ oz.; pure cyanide of potassium, ¼ oz.; gold transformed into chloride, ⅓ oz. The proportion of gold indicated is that of the metal employed, and it is not necessary to mind the weight of the chloride, if the proper amount of gold is dissolved in aqua regia.

Ten parts of metallic gold corresponds to about 18 parts of neutral chloride, or to 23 or 22 parts of acid chloride such as is usually sold. Steel articles, after cleansing by alkalies, must be passed rapidly through a very diluted solution of hydrochloric acid, wiped, and dipped into a very hot bath with an intense galvanic current at the beginning, which is gradually diminished by partly withdrawing the platinum anode.

Small articles of steel, such as pens, or watch hands, are threaded on a thin brass wire, and separated one from the other by glass beads. After cleansing, they are put into the boiling bath, rinsed, dried, and polished in hot and dry saw-dust.

It is preferable to give zinc, tin, lead, antimony, or the alloys of these metals, a previous coat of copper, or to begin the gilding in a hot gold electro-bath, nearly worn out, and to scratch-brush the articles carefully. The gilding is completed in a new hot bath, with a strong current.

PREPARATION OF THE GOLD BATH.

1. Put four-fifths of the distilled water into a porcelain dish, or an enameled cast-iron kettle, heated over a charcoal stove, and dissolve in it, by the aid of stirring, the crystallized phosphate of soda. When this is entirely dissolved, remove the liquor from the fire, filter if necessary, and allow it to cool off. 2. Place the gold in a glass flask, with ½ oz. of pure nitric acid and 1 oz. of pure hydrochloric acid. Heat slowly until the gold has dissolved, and then more rapidly to expel the excess of acid. There should remain a thick liquid of a blackish-red color. Remove the flask from the fire, and by cooling the contents form a brown-red crystalline mass. The cooling is important. 3. Dissolve in a porcelain dish, in half the remaining water, the bisulphite of soda and the cyanide of potassium. 4. Then dissolve the neutral chloride of gold in the remaining water, and pour it slowly, stirring with a glass rod, into the cold solution of phosphate of soda; add the solution of bisulphite and of cyanide. The whole liquor soon becomes colorless; the bath is then ready. If the chloride of gold were thrown into the solution of phosphate of soda while hot, there would be danger of a partial reduction of the gold in the form of a metallic powder.

The hot electro-gilding baths for small quantities of liquor are kept in porcelain dishes, but for large baths use enameled cast-iron kettles. The temperature may vary from 120° to 175° Fahr. Small articles, such as jewelry, are kept in the right hand with the conducting wire, and plunged and agitated in the bath. The left hand holds the anode of platinum wire, which is steeped more or less in the liquor, according to the surface of the articles to be gilt. Large pieces are suspended to one or more brass rods, and are not moved about. The gilding is very rapid, and a sufficient thickness is obtained after a few minutes. The shade of the gold deposit is modified by the amount of platinum anode dipping into the liquor. If it dips but a little, relatively to the surface of the articles, the gilding is pale; by immersing it more the shade will become deeper and deeper, until it is red. The platinum anode is connected by a conducting wire to the positive pole of the battery, and the conducting wire starting from the negative pole, touches or supports the articles to be gilt.

As a rule, it is preferable to replace the impoverished baths by fresh ones, instead of keeping up their strength by additions of metals, especially for small articles. When gilding large pieces, maintain the strength of the baths by successive additions of chloride of gold, or, what is better, of equal parts of gold ammonium and pure cyanide of potassium. In this manner baths may be made to last a long time, but they are open to the inconvenience of furnishing a red or green gilding, if many articles of copper or of silver have been gilt in them. Articles of copper or its alloys, should be perfectly cleansed, and may be passed through a very diluted solution of nitrate of binoxide of mercury.

Silver requires to be heated, dipped, and perfectly scratch-brushed. For this metal the gilding should be strong, in order to prevent the corners and raised parts from becoming white and bare ; and it is a good precaution to give it a coat of copper or brass, or a first gilding in an old bath.

2. Phosphate of soda, 14 oz.; bisulphite of soda, 3½ oz.; bicarbonate of potash and caustic potash, 1¾ oz. of each ; cyanide of potassium and pure gold for neutral chloride, ¼ oz. of each ; distilled water, 2⅛ gallons.

All the substances except the chloride of gold may be dissolved together, and filtered if necessary; then the solution of chloride of gold is added. This bath is heated at from 120° to 140° Fahr., and produces a very fine gilding, but it requires an intense electric current. It does not suit for the direct gilding of iron or steel.

3. Yellow prussiate of potash, 5¼ oz.; carbonate of potash, pure, 1¾ oz.; hydrochlorate of ammonia, ¾ oz.; pure gold for neutral chloride, ¼ oz.; water, 1 gallon. Dissolve the first three salts in hot water, and filter the solution ; after cooling add the gold solution, and boil for half an hour, taking care to replace the evaporated water.

4. Pure cyanide of potassium, 1¾ oz.; pure gold for neutral chloride, ¼ oz.; water, 5 pints. Dissolve the chloride of gold in the whole of the water, and add the cyanide, which dissolves and makes the liquor colorless. This bath may be employed with little regard to temperature, and is simple in its ingredients. Unfortunately it is not uniform in its working, as it will ungild one face of the object while the other face becomes gilt, or may produce a red gilding at the bottom and a yellow one at the top. These inconveniences will partly disappear by a long ebullition.

MANAGEMENT OF HOT GOLD BATHS.

The baths may be more concentrated, the quantity of water may be diminished, without changing the proportions of the salts and of the gold. But it is preferable to use diluted solutions, which deliver the metal in smaller quantity in a given time, but more homogeneous in substance. The articles should be kept in constant agitation; there is then no difference of specific gravity among the layers of the liquor, and the gilding possesses a uniform color. A foil or a wire of platinum is preferred to a soluble anode of gold when electro-gilding by the aid of heat, as it is not dissolved, and is more handy for regulating the intensity of the current, by immersing it more or less in the liquid. Thus with the same bath and battery three different shades can be obtained: a pale color, with the anode dipping but slightly; a yellow color, when the immersion is greater, and a red gold, if the whole anode is in the liquor.

In a bath of pink gold, composed of gold, copper and silver, by increasing or diminishing the length of the platinum anode in the liquor, the deposit will have a white, yellow, or red shade, as the various metals require different degrees of intensity for their reduction in the galvanic current.

In hot electro-gilding baths, and especially with small articles, keep them in the right hand constantly moving in the liquid, while the left hand is employed in changing the position of the platinum anode, so as to suit the surface and the nature of the articles, and obtain the desired shade.

The hot baths may have their strength maintained by successive additions of chloride of gold with a proper proportion of the other salts; but it is preferable to wear out the bath entirely and to prepare a new one. When a bath is exhausted, the gilding is red if much copper has been gilt in it, and green in the case of silver articles. It may then be used for a first coat upon objects which are to be finished in a new bath. Thus green or white golds result from the simultaneous deposit of gold or silver in various proportions; red gold from the alloy of copper and gold; and pink gold from the combination of gold, silver, and copper.

GREEN AND WHITE GOLDS.

Add to one of the above baths a solution of the double cyanide of silver and potassium, or a diluted solution of nitrate of silver, until the desired shade is obtained. The tints will vary from a leek-green to a very pale whitish-yellow. This kind of gilding mixed upon the same articles with red, yellow, or pink gold, will produce splendid effects of contrast, especially upon chased parts, where the green gold has a velvety luster.

RED GOLD.

Mix in suitable proportions the electro-copper bath already described with one of the baths for electro-gilding; or use an old bath in which a great many copper articles have been gilt, with an intense current of electricity. Yellow gilding may be made to pass to red, by heating it after it has been covered with a paste of acetate of copper, cream of tartar, and common salt. Plunge the heated piece into a weak solution of sulphuric acid, and carefully scratch-brush afterward.

PINK GOLD OR NEW GOLD.

This kind of gilding is the most difficult to obtain on account of the different tendency of the various metals to galvanic decomposition. Pink gilding, to be perfect, should present at the same time the red, yellow, and white shades, in such a manner that a practiced eye will distinguish them. The articles are first gilt yellow by the pyrophosphate bath for dipping, or by the hot electro-bath. Then, without drying, but keeping them in fresh water, small packages are made weighing from 1 to 2 oz. each; pass lightly through the mercurial solution, and then red gilt in an old and hot bath, where a great deal of copper has already been gilt, or in a new bath composed of 10 parts of hot electro-gilding bath, first formula, and 3 to 4 parts of the first coppering solution, with battery.

For imparting the whitish tint of articles gilt by stirring and of the gold alloy for jewelry, the red gilding is passed through a boiling and nearly exhausted bath of pyrophosphate, to which add one-tenth, or a twentieth, or a thirtieth of its volume of a silver bath, or simply a few drops of a concentrated solution of nitrate of silver. This gilding should be scratch-brushed or burnished, and may be chased, but the luster soon disappears on account of the proportion of copper.

To obtain the proper pink gilding, if the first deposit is unsatisfactory, plunge the articles for a few seconds into a mixture of 5 parts of sulphuric acid to 1 of nitric acid. The copper and silver are dissolved, and the yellow gilding reappears, upon which the operation may be begun anew. Besides the variations of color in gilding due to the dipping of the anodes more or less into the bath, and to the strength of the electric current, moving the articles about in the bath will at all times enable the operator to vary the color of the deposit from pale straw-yellow to a very dark red. The temperature of the solution likewise influences the color of the deposit, the color being lightest when the solution is cold, and gradually becoming darker as the temperature increases.

GILDING WATCH PARTS.

In gilding small articles for watchmakers, gold is seldom directly applied upon the copper; there is generally a preliminary operation, called graining, by which a grained and slightly dead appearance is given to the articles.

PREPARATION OF THE SILVER PARTS.

Marks of the file are obliterated by a rubbing upon a wet stone, and lastly upon an oilstone. Any oil or grease is removed by boiling the parts for a few minutes in a solution made of 100 parts of water and 10 of caustic soda or potash; rinse in clear water, which should wet them entirely if all the oil has been removed. The articles are threaded upon a brass wire; cleanse them rapidly in the compound acids for a bright luster, and dry them carefully in white wood saw-dust. The pieces are fastened upon the even side of a block of cork by brass pins with flat heads. The parts are then thoroughly rubbed over with a brush, entirely free from grease, and charged with a paste of water and very fine pumice-stone powder. Move the brush in circles, in order not to rub one side more than the other; thoroughly rinse in clean water, and no particle of pumice-dust should remain upon the pieces, or the cork. Next place the cork and the pieces into a weak mercurial solution, which very slightly whitens the copper, composed of—water, two and one-fifth gallons, nitrate or binoxide of mercury, one-fourteenth of an ounce; sulphuric acid, one-seventh of an ounce. The pieces are passed quickly through the solution, and then rinsed. This operation gives strength to the graining which, without it, possesses no adherence.

GRAINING POWDERS.

1. Silver in impalpable powder, 1 oz.; cream of tartar, finely pulverized and passed through a silk sieve, 10 oz.; common salt, pulverized and sifted as above, 2 lbs. 2. Silver powder, 1 oz.; cream of tartar, 4 to 5 oz.; common salt, white and clean, 13 oz. 3. Silver powder, 1 oz.; cream of tartar, 3 oz.; common salt, white and clean, 2 lbs. All these substances should be as pure as possible, and perfectly dry. Cream of tartar is generally dry; common salt often needs, before or after it has been pulverized, a thorough drying in a porcelain or silver dish, in which it is kept stirred with a glass rod or a silver spoon. The mixture of the three substances must be thorough, and effected at a moderate and protracted heat. The graining is the coarser the more common salt there is in the mixture; and it is the finer and more condensed as the proportion of cream of tartar is greater, but it is then more difficult to scratch-brush.

SILVER POWDER.

The silver powder is obtained by immersing cleansed copper plates in a very diluted solution of nitrate of silver made with distilled water. The more diluted the solution is, the finer is the precipitate of silver upon the copper, and the more easily it is removed. In a glass or porcelain vessel ⅔ of an ounce of crystalized nitrate of silver are dissolved in 2¼ gallons of distilled water, and 5 or 6 bands of cleansed copper ¾ of an inch wide are placed in it. These bands should be long enough to allow of a portion being above the liquid. The whole is kept in a dark place for 24 hours, and now and then stirred with the copper bands. This motion is sufficient to loosen the deposited silver, and present fresh copper surfaces to the action of the liquor. When no more silver deposits on the copper, the operation is completed, and there remains a blue solution of nitrate of copper. The silver powder is washed by decantation, or upon a filter, until there remains nothing of the copper solution. It is then carefully dried, avoiding contact with hard bodies. Nuremberg powder is produced by grinding a mixture of honey and silver foil upon a ground-glass plate with a muller until the proper fineness is obtained. The silver is separated by dissolving the honey in boiling water, and washing the deposited metal in a filter, until there is no remaining trace of honey. The silver is then carefully dried at a gentle heat.

GRAINING.

A thin paste made of one of the above powders and water is spread by means of a spatula upon the watch parts held upon the cork. The cork itself is placed upon an earthenware dish, to which a rotating movement is imparted by the left hand. An oval brush with close bristles, held in the right hand, rubs the watch parts in every direction, but always with a rotary motion. A new quantity of the paste is added two or three times, and rubbed in the manner indicated. The more the brush and the cork are turned the rounder becomes the grain, which is a good quality; and the more paste added the larger the grain.

When the desired grain is obtained, the pieces are washed and then scratch-brushed. The wire brushes employed, which usually come from Nuremberg, are made of brass wires as fine as hair, very stiff and springy. It is necessary to anneal them upon an even fire to different degrees ; one soft, or half annealed, for the first operation of uncovering the grain ; one harder, for bringing up the luster ; and one very soft, or fully annealed, used before gilding for removing any marks which may have been made by the preceding tool, and for scratch-brushing after the gilding, which, like the graining, must be done by giving a rotary motion to the tool. Decoctions of liquorice or saponaire are employed in this operation.

RESISTS.

If it happens that the same watch part is composed of copper and steel, this latter metal requires to be preserved against the action of the cleansing acids and of the graining mixture, by a composition called resist. This consists in covering the pinions and other steel parts with a fatty composition, which is sufficiently hard to resist the tearing action of the bristle and wire brushes, and insoluble in the alkalies of the gilding bath. Yellow wax, 2 oz.; translucent colophony, 3½ oz.; extra fine red sealing-wax, 1⅓ oz.; impalpable peroxide of iron or polishing rouge, 1 oz. Melt the colophony and sealing-wax in a porcelain dish upon a water bath, and afterward add the yellow wax. When the whole is thoroughly fluid, gradually add the rouge, and stir with a wooden or glass rod. Withdraw the heat, but continue the stirring until the mixture becomes solid, otherwise all the oxide of iron will fall to the bottom of the mixture. The flat parts to receive this resist are slightly heated, and then covered with the mixture which melts and is easily spread.

For covering steel pinions, employ a small gouge of copper or brass fixed to a wooden handle. The metallic part of the gouge is heated upon an alcohol lamp, and a small quantity of resist is taken with it. The composition soon melts, and, by turning the tool around the steel pinion, this becomes coated. Use a scratch-brush with long wires, as their flexibility prevents the removal of the composition.

When the resist is to be removed after gilding, place the parts in warm oil or into tepid turpentine, then into a very hot soap-water or alkaline solution, and lastly into fresh water. Scratch-brush and dry in warm saw-dust of white wood. The holes of the pinions are cleaned and polished with small pieces of very soft white wood, the friction of which is sufficient to restore the primitive luster.

The gilding of parts composed of copper and steel requires the greatest care, as the slightest rust destroys their future usefulness. Should some gold deposit upon the steel, it should be removed by rubbing with a piece of wood and impalpable pumice-dust, tin putty, or rouge.

GILDING SEVERAL COLORS ON SAME OBJECT.

Again, when it is desired to obtain gildings of several colors upon the same object, resists, generally made of some kind of varnish, are used; after having gilt an article of a uniform red or green color, it is covered with a fat varnish, made drying by the addition of chromate of lead, at those places which are to resist the action of the new bath. By means of resists and successive baths, several different shades can be obtained upon the same object. The resist varnishes are applied with a brush or pencil, and should be thoroughly dried in a stove before placing the object into another solution. These varnishes may be colored with various oxides or colored salts, in order to facilitate their use upon those places which should be sharply marked ; chromate of lead and artificial ultramarine blue are well suited for the purpose.

Resist varnishes are also used for preserving the reverse parts of articles which have to receive the gilding only on the front. When the operation is finished, the resist is easily removed by a washing, first with essence of turpentine, gasoline, benzine or benzole, and then with alcohol ; when benzole is used, it is sufficient to wash the article in boiling water, and then to dry it in warm saw-dust of fir-wood. It comes out perfectly clean. This is not always the case with rectified turpentine, and it may be necessary to plunge the object into a hot alkaline lye, then to rinse and dry it in warm saw-dust.

MODUS OPERANDI OF GILDING BY BATTERY.

After the preparations described, the gilding may be effected by some of the processes already mentioned. Hot baths must not be employed for those pieces covered with the resist. Heat one-eighth of an ounce of finely laminated and pure gold in order to destroy all organic substances, dissolve in a glass flask with three-sixteenths of an ounce of pure nitric acid, and three-eighths of an ounce of pure hydrochloric acid. When the gold is dissolved, evaporate the excess of acids, leaving in the flasks a syrupy dark-red liquid ; the whole is then removed from the fire and allowed to cool. Dissolve the chloride of gold in about 2 oz. of distilled water, and pour into a large glass vessel. Dilute with about a pint of distilled water, and pour into the liquor a certain excess of pure ammonia, which precipitates the gold in the state of a yellow powder of ammoniuret of gold, or fulminate of gold, which is a detonating powder when dry. The proportion of ammonia is sufficient, when a new quantity of this reagent, being added to the clear liquid above the settled powder, does not produce any new precipitate.

The clear liquor is decanted and kept among the saved waste. Collect the settled powder upon a small filter, previously wetted with distilled water then wash with distilled water until all ammoniacal smell has disappeared. The filter and its contents are afterward put into a glass or porcelain vessel with a quart of distilled water and three-eights of an ounce of pure cyanide of pottasium, which rapidly destroys the gold and passes through the filter. The whole is filtered again, boiled for 15 to 20 minutes, filtered again, and left to cool. The bath obtained is excellent for gilding the most delicate watch parts, with an electric current regulated to suit the surfaces to the gilt.

Several of these baths, in various degrees of exhaustion, are generally kept in glass or porcelain vessels flat-bottomed, and holding from 7 to 9 pints within a depth of 4 to 5 inches. The articles to be gilt are suspended to metallic holders, connected with the zinc pole of a battery, and of a shape appropriate to the nature and form of the watch parts. One or more platinum wires are used for anodes, and are disposed in the center or round the bath. The battery most generally employed is composed of three, four, five or six small Daniell's elements. Those with balloons, on account of their constancy, should be preferred.

The slower the gold deposit, the finer and more adherent it is. When the coating is sufflcient, wash the articles in clean water, and fix again upon the cork in order to proceed to the last scratch-brushing with a decoction of liquorice, or of horse-chestnut.

GILDING THIN WIRES.

Gilt silver is fine; gilt copper is half fine; and copper or brass alone is false. At the present time, nearly all gilt wire is gilt by electricity; the baths and the battaries are the same as those already mentioned, but for the success of the operation a certain disposition of the apparatus is required. Upon a brick furnace, which may be heated either with solid fuel or gas, is a cast-iron enameled kettle, about 3 feet long, 18 inches wide, and 4 to 7 inches deep, for holding the gold bath. If gas is used as fuel, the burner should be an elleptic ring with 25 or 30 jets attached to it, or the same kettle may be used as a cold bath if desired, the fire being optional. At one end of the apparatus, near the battery, are two wooden stands supporting an iron rod which passes through a certain number of wooden spools carrying the wire to be gilt. These spools turn freely upon the rod, and the unwound wires, before dipping into the bath, are pressed against a copper or brass rod, connected with the negative, zinc, pole of the battery; thus the wires are connected with this pole. The wires dip into the bath to about two-thirds of its depth, and are kept stretched by small grooved pulleys of glass, porcelain or ivory, rolling freely upon glass or ivory axes, which are kept near the bottom by supports screwed on the top edges of the kettle.

At the bottom of the bath, and crossing the wires to be gilt, are two or more platinum wires, the vertical branches of which communicate with the positive, or carbon, pole. These platinum anodes must nowhere touch wires to be gilt, as these two kinds of wire represent the two poles of the battery in the bath. At the other end of the apparatus is another series of wooden reels, upon which the gilt wire is wound up. These reels are fixed to the square iron axis which traverses them, and which is turned by gearing, slowly enough to ensure a good gilding to the wire, during its passage through the bath. After passing through the gilding bath, the wires are rinsed and dried by winding over two wooden rollers revolving freely upon their axis, and plunged by means of grooved rollers into the first trough, filled with a weak solution of cyanide of potassium, which cleans and brightens the gilding; they then pass into the second trough filled with water, which is constantly replaced, which removes the salts from the wires.

The drying rollers, covered with several layers of calico, are moved by gear in opposite directions; the wires are thoroughly dried in a flat tube, kept at a dull red heat in the furnace. In a kettle of the size named, 20 wires may be gilt at the same time.

Copper wires are generally previously silvered and passed once through a draw plate, to avoid the cleansing process before gilding. The more intense the battery, or the slower the wires pass through the bath, so will the deposit of gold be increased; and it will be well to weigh the bobbins before and after the operation, for which purpose the spools for winding up and winding out should be of the same weight. This gilding requires constant supervision, either for uniting the broken wires, the severed parts of which may touch the anodes, and stop the operation; or for regulating the intensity of the battery, which, if too powerful, will produce a red gilding, or, if too weak, a green gilding.

Baths of double cyanide of gold and patassium are employed cold or slightly tempid; baths with phosphate and bisulphite of soda are used for hot electro-gilding, but they are concentrated until the proportion of water is one-half of that indicated. As the platinum anodes do not make up for the metallic loss of the bath, it is frequently necessary to add new portions of metal and salts, in the manner already described.

Pure gold wire is sometimes gilt, in order to impart to it a more uniform and deeper shade. After being gilt the wire is passed through the draw-plate or the rollers. By the draw-plate it is diminished by about one-fourth or one-half of a number to remove the dulness of the deposit, and bring up the luster. When the gilt wire is flattened between the rollers, its surface is bright or dull according to the state of the surface of the rollers. Silvering, or any other metallic electro-deposit upon thin wires, can be effected in a similar manner.

GILDING WITH A DEAD LUSTER.

1. By the slow deposit of a large proportion of gold. This gilding is very durable, but dull and earthy in appearance, and is costly.

2. By acids; giving a dead luster to the metallic surface, before gilding, and by the processes indicated in the cleansing operations. This is employed for small articles, or when gilding by dipping, for bronze articles, or large embossed work.

3. With frosted silver, by depositing upon the object to be gilt a coat of frosted silver, and then gilding in a good bath; this method is expensive, the burnished parts are greenish, and the intermediary coat of silver is more easily blackened by sulphur fumes than gold.

4. By depositing from a solution of sulphate of copper decomposed by a battery a coat of this metal, which possesses a pink dead luster. The whole is rapidly passed through the compound acids for a bright luster, and the mercurial solution, and then gilt in a good bath. When the dead luster obtained in the bath is perfect, the compound acids may be dispensed with, and merely place the article in the mercurial solution before it is gilt. This mode is generally preferred, as the gilding is very handsome in luster and color. The burnished parts will be red, if vinegar or soap-water is used; and of a fine yellow color, if the burnishing tool be wetted with a decoction of flax-seed, or of marsh-mallow root. If the gold deposit is of insufficient thickness, it will blacken in time, by the oxidization of the intermediate coat of copper.

5. Dead luster by mercury, or the old process of gilding by fire, which furnishes the most durable gilding, although costly, as already described.

GILDING FOR POTTERIES.

Much of the porcelain and china ware sold is gilded or painted after it leaves the potteries, by houses which devote themselves specially to this kind of work. But there is also a kind having a *gold* luster, as it is called, which is done at the manufacturies. It is best to do it on a body specially prepared of 4 parts clay, 4 parts flint, 4 parts kaolin, and 6 parts feldspar. This should be covered with a glaze, of 60 parts litharge, 36 parts feldspar, and 15 flint.

PREPARATION OF GOLD LUSTER.

Dissolve first in the cold, and then with heat, 48 grains of fine gold in 288 grains of an aqua regia, composed of 1 ounce of nitric acid and 3 ounces of muriatic acid ; add to that solution 4½ grains of grain tin, bit by bit ; and then pour some of that compound solution into 20 grains of balsam of sulphur diluted with 10 grains of oil of turpentine. The balsam of sulphur is prepared by heating a pint of linseed oil, and 2 ounces of flour of sulphur, stirring them continually till the mixture begins to boil ; it is then cooled, by setting the vessel in cold water ; after which it is stirred afresh, and strained through linen. The above ingredients, after being well mixed, are to be allowed to settle for a few minutes ; then the remainder of the solution of gold is to be poured in, and the whole is to be triturated till the mass has assumed such a consistence that the pestle will stand upright in it; lastly, there must be added to the mixture 30 grains of oil of turpentine, which being ground in, the gold luster is ready to be applied. If the luster is too light or pale, more gold must be added, and if it have not a sufficiently violet or purple tint, more tin must be used.

ANOTHER GOLD LUSTER.

Dissolve a gold dollar in aqua regia with a gentle heat. To the solution when cool, add 2 grains of grain tin, which will immediately dissolve. Prepare a mixture of half an ounce of balsam of sulphur with a little essence of turpentine, beating them together till they assume the appearance of milk. Pour this mixture into the solution of gold and tin, drop by drop, with continual stirring ; and place the whole in a warm s.tuation for some time.

It is absolutely necessary to apply this luster only upon an enamel or glaze which has already passed through the fire, otherwise the sulphur would tarnish the composition.

Balsam of sulphur is made by adding two ounces powdered brimstone to a pint of heated linseed oil, stirring until thoroughly melted and straining through a piece of muslin.

These lusters are applied with most advantage upon chocolate and other dark grounds. Much skill is required in their firing, and a perfect acquaintance with the quality of the glaze on which they are applied.

For other methods it is necessary first to prepare a *Flux*. Brown gold is gold with a copper alloy of about ⅓ ; in green gold the alloy is silver in the proportion of 6 silver to 20 gold.

GOLD FLUX.

Borax, 11 parts ; litharge, 5½ ; oxide of silver, 1. Grind very fine. Melt in a crucible. Pulverize and regrind for use.

BURNISH GOLD (BROWN).

Brown oxide of gold, 12 parts ; mercury, 8 ; oxide of silver, 2 ; white lead, 1. Grind very fine in an earthenware mortar, and mix with spirits of turpentine for use. The parts combine very easily. The white lead is the flux in this case.

BURNISH GOLD (GREEN GOLD).

Green gold, 12 parts ; mercury, 7½ ; oxide of silver, 1½ ; flux (as above) 1½. First put the gold alone in an earthenware mortar ; place over the fire ; heat to a red heat ; pour in now mercury to the extent of 4 times the weight of the whole mixture. Stir with an iron rod until perfectly mixed, and then pour the whole into a vessel of water. When it can be handled, pour off the water ; collect amalgam into a piece of muslin ; squeeze out the surplus mercury (saving this for future operations) ; throw this amalgam into nitrous acid to dissolve out the mercury. Wash the gold in clear water several times, and finally mix with fresh mercury, the silver and the flux as above. Grind very fine and mix with spirits of turpentine for use.

CHEAP OR BRONZE GOLD.

Burnish gold (see above), 125 parts ; oxide of copper, 4 ; mercury, 2 ; Flux, 1. Dissolve the copper in aqua fortis; precipitate it (put an iron rod into the solution) ; gather and wash the precipitate, and then mix with the other ingredients, and finally with spirits of turpentine. It may be be made brighter or darker by varying the proportions of gold or copper. Gold gives the brightness.

GILDING CHINA BY BATTERY.

The ingenious process recently introduced in France for electrotyping on a non-conducting material, such as china, &c., is likely to prove of peculiar value, both for practical and artistic purposes, but is evidently one requiring much care in order to insure a fair degree of success. It appears that sulphur is dissolved in the oil of spike to form a sirupy consistence ; and then chloride of gold or chloride of platinum is dissolved in sulphuric ether, and the two solutions are in this state mingled under a gentle heat. The compound is next evaporated until of the thickness of ordinary paint, in which condition it is applied with a brush to such portions of the china, glass, or other fabrics, as are desired to be covered, according to the design or pattern, with the electro-metalic deposit. The objects are baked in the usual way before they are immersed in the bath.

FRENCH SIZE OR CLEAR COLE.

A good method of making size, practiced in France, is to cut up rabbit skins (free of hair) into fine shreds and boil them in a water bath as glue is boiled. A part of the skin will remain undissolved. The fluid is, therefore strained, and the clear part is kept for use. A hot solution of white vitriol (salt of zinc) and alum is next prepared—an ounce of vitriol to a quarter of an ounce of alum for every quart of water. Of this a half pint is added to a quart of the thin clear rabbit skin glue. It is left to to thicken—then cut up to dry. This glue when thoroughly dry is used in the proportions of one-half a pound to a gallon of water. It makes a strong thick size.

EARLY ILLUMINATED WORK.

The gilding employed by the old illuminators was of two kinds, flat, and raised or embossed. The former was used for laying a large smooth surface for painting upon, and in many cases even for scrolls and ornaments, but chiefly for shading and putting in the highest light on such colors as reds, browns, and yellows. The raised gilding was principally used for nimbi, or glories round the heads of saints, for lines, background letters, and small ornaments and leaves.

GILDING WITH WATER GOLD SIZE.

Dip a camel hair pencil in the gold size, the same way as liquid water-colors are used, and apply it to every part of the illumination which is to be gilt. Where the gold is intended to be raised, lay on as many coats as will raise the work sufficiently; but take care to do it all as smoothly as possible, so that no ridges may appear, for they give the gold a streaky appearance which must be avoided. Let it stand quite half-and-hour to harden well. Previous to putting the gold leaf on, breathe upon the size to render it sufficiently adhesive, and apply the gold leaf immediately. The success of burnishing results from practice, and is influenced by the heat of the room; try gently with the burnisher, and if it glides about easily, it is ready. Indenting a pattern on gold is best done by the point of an ivory tracer, or by a thick darning needle. The indented lines may be drawn with the worn point of a penknife.

IMITATION GILDING.

There are two methods of imitating gilding. One for temporary purposes—such as theatrical scenery etc., etc., is by the use of Dutch metal, or Dutch gold, which is simply brass or copper foil. The gilding is effected with Japanner's gold-size, as already described for real gold. Dutch metal soon turns green on exposure unless varnished, and even then it discolors easily.

The other method is to use a silver or even tin-foil, which is still cheaper, and cover with a varnish of good yellow tint—like the ormolu. A good imitation is also obtained by varnishing the ordinary tin-plate, after polishing it somewhat with pumice-stone and water. Any varnish with a decidedly yellow tinge will answer. None of these methods, however, are durable. A first coat of thin shelllac-varnish ensures a better adhesion of any subsequent coat of varnish; but this also will peel under the alternate expansion and contraction of the metal below.

GILDING FOR PRINTERS.

Hat tips and other sized muslin work are done as described in section on Book Gilding. But work on paper—generally glazed—is first printed with gold-size instead of ink and the gold-leaf laid on as in any ordinary gilding with leaf. The leaf is patted down and the superfluous gold brushed away. In lithographic printing the gilding process is precisely the same. Dutch metal is much used in label work. The size in this case should be strong, and used as abundantly as it can be—as metal is apt to come off and make the work look shabby. In bronzing, the powder is rubbed lightly over the impression printed in size with a piece of raw cotton well filled with the powder. The finer the bronze the more economical the work. Gold in powder is sometimes used.

SILKS, SATINS, WOOLENS, IVORY, BONE, &C.,

May be readily gilded by immersing them in a *solution of neutral terchloride of gold* (1 of the *salt,* and 3 to 6 of *water*), and then exposing them to the action of *hydrogen gas.* The latter part of the process may readily be performed by pouring some *dilute sulphuric acid* on *zinc* or *iron filings,* in a wide-mouthed bottle, and placing it under a jar or similar vessel, inverted, at the top of which the articles to be gilded are suspended. *Flowers* or *other ornamental designs* may be produced by painting them on the surface with a camel-hair pencil dipped in the solution. The design, after a few minutes' exposure to the hydrogen, shines with all the splendor of the purest gold, and will not tarnish on exposure to the air, or in washing.

SILVERING.

WHITENING WITH SILVER IN A POT.

This operation is still employed for whitening small wares for which durability is of secondary importance, and which simply require the whiteness of silver; such are hooks and eyes, or buttons. This whitening is made as follows :—

1. Dissolve a certain quantity of pure granulated silver in double its weight of pure nitric acid. The solution is largely diluted with water, and the metal is precipitated in heavy white clods by common salt or hydrochloric acid. All the nitrate of silver has been decomposed when a further addition of hydrochloric acid or common salt to the clear supernatant liquid does not produce any turbidness. The clear liquors are then thrown away, and the chloride of silver obtained is washed several times, to deprive it of all free acid. If this precipitate is to be kept some time before use, it should be removed from the sunlight, which blackens it rapidly. The chloride of silver, with a little water, is thoroughly mixed with at least 80 times its weight of finely powdered bitartrate of potash, and kept in a stoneware pot.

2. Pure silver for making the chloride, 1 part; powdered cream tartar, salt, 83 parts of each; a few spoonfuls of the paste thrown in, and dissolved in boiling water contained in a pure copper kettle.

The articles are dipped into this bath by a hook, or in a basket of wire gauze, such as indicated in receipt for gilding by dipping. Or have another basin of copper, shallow and perforated with holes, which rests against the upper sides of the kettle. By means of handles, this basin can be removed at once with its con-

tents. Stir the articles with a wooden spatula; and at each
operation add a quantity of paste proportioned to the surfaces to
be whitened These baths do not work well when freshly made,
but improve as they are more used. They acquire a dark green
tint, due to the copper which is dissolved, and which takes the
place of the deposited silver. Varnishing, coloring, and cleansing
may be done in aquafortis; but these cleansing methods are inferior to those employed for gilding; in general, use the worn-
out acids of gilders. Brighten the articles by friction with saw-
dust. The smallest particle of iron, zinc, or tin introduced into
the whitening bath imparts a red color to the brass or copper
articles in the liquor. The iron is separated by a magnet; the
zinc is dissolved in pickles of hydrochloric or sulphuric acid,
which, when cold, do not sensibly corrode the copper articles;
tin or lead must be picked out by hand. If the operation has
not succeeded, the articles are plunged for a few seconds into a
boiling solution of water, $2\frac{1}{4}$ gallons; nitrate of silver, $3\frac{1}{4}$ oz.;
ordinary cyanide of potassium, 21 oz. This bath retains its
strength for a long time, and increases the brightness and whiteness of the deposit. The process of silvering by dipping has
nearly superseded this method.

PLATED SILVER

Is obtained by rolling together a plate of copper of the first
quality, and one of silver; these are either welded, or simply
united by placing their hot and clean surfaces together, wetted
with a concentrated solution of nitrate of silver. The two metals
are reduced and drawn out about equally by the pressure of rolls,
and long sheets or bands of silvered metal are thus obtained, with
which a great many articles may be manufactured. By this
mode of operation, a great quantity of material is lost, as the
objects have to be cut out from a sheet entirely silvered, and the
waste retains a large proportion of that metal; the cut sections
present parts without silver, which must be hidden by ledges, or
by silvering by another method. There is also the absolute necessity of employing pure copper, which is more costly, less
sonorous, and not so tough as its alloys; but the greatest defect
of the process is the difference of thickness of the silver, according to the shape of the object. Raised surfaces are the most exposed to friction, and it is just there that the coat of silver is the
thinnest; the conditions are reversed with electro-silvering, and
the parts in relief receive a more abundant deposit of silver,
which is a satisfactory result. The best plated silver is manufactured by applying upon an ingot of pure copper weighing 9

parts, another ingot of pure silver weighing 1 part, to coat one
side only; add another part of silver, if it is intended to coat both
sides. The two are rolled together until the desired thickness is
obtained.

The silver of the plated metal will be bright if the rollers are
well polished, and dull with rough rollers. The only solder which
does not injure plated silver is tin solder ; and when the objects
manufactured are required to resist a warm temperature, nuts
and screws are employed. The electro-plating of old wares made
from copper with a covering of silver, is often difficult. Supposing it is required to electro-plate an old cruet-stand, the
bottom is separated from the wire, either by unsoldering or un-
screwing. Smooth by emery cloth, or pumice-stone and water,
or by powdered bath-brick brushed over with a hard brush.
Spots of verdigris are removed with a few drops of hydrochloric
acid. The great difficulty consists in giving a good electro-deposit
upon the edges or mounts where there may be some lead or lead
solder ; apply to such parts, with a rather soft brush, a solution
made by dissolving 4 oz. of mercury in nitric acid, and adding
about half a pint of cold water. This solution is lightly brushed
over the lead mounts only ; the article and brush are then to be
well rinsed, and the brush and plain water applied in the same
way.

The solution of mercury will turn the edges black, or dark
gray, but the subsequent brushing will render them bright again
The frame when well rinsed is ready for the depositing bath.
If, on its first immersion, any black spots appear, the frame may be
removed, again brushed over, and finally returned to the bath. If
the edges do not receive the coating of silver as readily as the other
parts, the solution may require a little more cyanide, or a greater
battery power, or an increase in the surface of the anode   These
lead edges may be prepared for receiving the silver deposit by a
previous coat of copper applied as follows :—The edges are
plunged into a solution of sulphate of copper, with a little free
sulphuric acid in it ; then, by touching the lead edge with an iron
wire, it is immediately coated with a bright deposit of copper,
which is rinsed and becomes a good conductor for the further
electro-deposit of silver. The coating of tin underneath the bottom of cruet frames is very difficult to plate, unless in a solution
made expressly for it ; therefore it is preferable to remove it
either with abrading materials, or with nitric acid employed with
care. This process of depositing copper will be found useful not
only for old plated ware, but also for many articles on which are
found unruly spots of tin solder.

SILVERING WITH SILVER FOIL.

This method is never practiced except upon objects **already** manufactured, in their definite shape ; and is adapted to **all** kinds of copper, bronze, or brass. It is, in certain respects, superior to plated silver ; but is very difficult of execution, **and** has less adhesion to the metal underneath. After annealing **the** articles, they are thrown whilst hot into a bath of sulphuric acid with a small proportion of hydrochloric and nitric acids. They have then a dull and dead luster, owing to a multitude of small holes, which are so many points of attachment for the silver foil. The objects, thus prepared, are tightly fixed upon **an iron rod,** which is held in a vice. Their temperature is raised **to about** 800° F., by means of incandescent charcoal put at **the** proper place, so as to open the pores of the metal, which, **by cooling** afterward, will imprison the silver applied. The **silver foils,** taken from the book with small tweezers, are cut to the proper size upon a cushion with an ivory or steel knife. After each foil is deposited upon the object, it is made to adhere by a light pressure of a rag pad, and afterward by the friction of a steel burnishing tool. The parts of the silver foil which do not adhere are removed with a soft brush. Gold-beaters prepare silver foil either with bright or dead luster. The latter is made to adhere only by the pressure of the pad, and not by the burnishing tool. This dead luster cannot compare in fineness with that obtained by the battery ; however, it resists handling and the sulphur gases of the atmosphere better. Articles thus silvered are only burnished after all the silver foils have been applied ; round or cylindrical objects are burnished upon the lathe, other forms by the hand ; there are always places and lines showing the vibrations of the burnishing tool. This method of silvering is only employed for very large objects, such as high chandeliers and other church ornaments. Spoons and forks may be covered with silver foil, as follows :—First, slightly silver with a dead luster in a silver bath by dipping ; heat, and then cover with silver foil, forcing the silver foils into the pores of the metal underneath, by the pressure of an iron scratch-brush striking vertically. Burnish by the usual method ; it is impossible to obtain a dead luster by this method.

COLD SILVERING BY RUBBING,

with the thumb, or cork, or a brush. The results are better than those by the whitening process, but not very durable ; the method is useful to repair slight defects upon more durable silverings, and to produce mixtures of gold and silver, or gold, upon slightly gilt objects, thus avoiding the use of resist varnishes. Make a paste by thoroughly grinding in a porcelain mortar or with a muller, and, as far as practicable, not in the light ;—1. Water, 3¼ to 5 oz. ; white fused nitrate of silver, or, preferably, the chloride, 7 oz. ; binoxalate of potash, 10¼ oz. ; bitartrate of potash, 10¼ oz. ; common salt, 15 oz. ; sal ammoniac, 2¾ oz. 2. Chloride of silver, 3¼ oz. ; bitrartrate of potash, 7 oz. ; common salt, 10¼ oz.

When finely pulverized in a porcelain mortar, triturate it under a muller upon a plate of ground glass until there is no granular feeling. Keep the paste in a porcelain pot, or in a black glass vessel, to preserve it from the light, which decomposes it rapidly. When about to use it, add a little water so as to form a thin paste, which is applied with a brush or pencil upon the cleansed articles of copper, or upon those gilt by dipping, or even upon those gilt by the battery, provided that the coating is thin enough to allow the copper to decompose the silver paste through the coat of gold ; allow the paste to dry naturally, or with the aid of a gentle heat. The chemical reaction is more or less complete, according to the thickness of the gold deposit, and the dry paste is of a pink shade, or entirely green. The salts are removed by a thorough rinsing in cold water, and the silver appears with a fine frosted appearance, the brightness of which may be increased by a few seconds' immersion in a very diluted solution of sulphuric acid, or of cyanide of potassium. This silvering bears the action of the wire brush and of the burnishing tool very well, and it may also be oxidized. Should a first silvering not be found sufficiently durable, after scratch-brushing, apply a second or a third coat. This silvering is not so adhering or white on pure copper, as upon a gilt surface. For the reflectors of lanterns the paste is rubbed upon the reflector with a fine linen pad ; then with another rag, a thin paste of Spanish white, or similar substance, is spread over the reflector and allowed to dry. Rubbing with a fine and clean linen rag will restore the luster and whiteness of the plated silver.

FOR PLATED SILVER REFLECTORS.

A bath made of water, 1¾ pint ; nitrate of chloride of silver, 2 oz. ; cyanide of potassium, 10¼ oz. Add sufficient Spanish white, or levigated chalk, in fine powder, to produce a thin paste, which is kept in a well closed pot. This paste is spread by a brush or a pad of old linen, all over the surface of the reflector, and allowed almost to dry, when it is briskly rubbed over by another clean dry rag of old linen.

SILVERING BY DIPPING IN A WARM BATH.

For small articles a bath is made by dissolving in an enameled cast-iron kettle in 2 galls. of water 17½ oz. of ordinary cyanide of potassium. Also dissolve 5½ oz. of fused nitrate of silver in 1¾ pint of water contained in a glass or porcelain vessel.

The second solution is gradually poured into the first one Stir with a glass rod. The white or grayish-white precipitate produced soon dissolves, and the remaining liquor is filtered if a perfectly clear bath is desired. When brought to the boiling-point it will immediately silver the cleansed copper articles plunged in it. The objects must be quickly withdrawn. The silvering should immediately follow the cleansing, although the rinsings after each operation should be thorough and complete. This bright and light silvering is adapted for set jewelery, which cannot be scratch-brushed without flattening the clasps, and to which a bright luster is absolutely necessary as a substitute for the foil of burnished silver placed under the precious stones or real jewelery. The employment of the solution of nitrate of binoxide of mercury is useless, and even injurious for this bath. It is useless to keep up the strength of the solution by new additions of cyanide and silver salt ; thus reinvigorated, it gives results far inferior to those of the former solution. The bath should, therefore, be worked out as long as the silvering is satisfactory, and when exhausted put away with the waste. With this process a battery and a soluble anode may be used to obtain a more durable deposit ; but the operation is no longer a simple dipping, and properly belongs to electro-silvering by heat. A solution, which, when boiling, produces a very fine silver coat, with a dead, or partly dead, luster, upon cleansed coppers, is made by dissolving with the aid of heat, in a well-scoured copper kettle, distilled water, 9 pints ; ferrocyanide of potassium, 21 oz. ; carbonate of potash, 14 oz. When the liquid boils add the well-washed chloride obtained from 1 oz. of pure silver This should boil for about half an hour, and be filtered before using ; part of the silver deposits upon the copper kettle, and should be removed when a new bath is prepared. On account of this inconvenience the process has been nearly abandoned, although the products are remarkably fine. All the dipping silvering baths, which contain a comparatively great excess of cyanide of potassium to the proportion of the silver salt, will silver welt copper articles perfectly cleansed, even in the cold ; whereas this property diminishes in proportion to the increase of the amount of silver in the bath, or with the decrease of the amount of cyanide.

SADDLERY AND CARRIAGE WARES.

For small articles, partly copper and partly iron, such as those used for saddlery and carriage wares, a particular process of silvering is used. The bath is composed of :—Water, 9 pints ; caustic potash, 6 oz. ; bicarbonate of potash, 3½ oz. ; cyanide of potassium, 2 oz. ; fused nitrate of silver, ¾ oz. The cyanide, caustic potash, and bicarbonate are dissolved in 7 pints of water in an enameled cast-iron kettle, then the remaining quart of water, in which the nitrate of silver has been separately dissolved, is added to the former solution. For the silvering operation a certain quantity of articles is cleansed, thoroughly rinsed, and put into a small enameled kettle. Enough of the silver bath is poured in to cover the articles entirely, and the whole is brought to a boil for a few seconds, and stirred with a wooden spatula.

When the silvering appears satisfactory, the liquor employed is put with the saved waste ; the same liquid is never used for two batches of articles. This process gives a somewhat durable silvering with a dead luster, of a grayish white, which is increased in whiteness and brightness by soap and burnishing.

SILVERING BY DIPPING IN A COLD BATH.

As the bath is cold it is always ready for use, and the deposit is finer and more unalterable, because only chemically pure silver is deposited, without any mixture of subsalts. The bath is formed of bisulphite of soda, to which is added nitrate of silver, until it begins to be dissolved with difficulty. It is therefore with a double sulphite of soda and silver that the cold silvering by dipping is effected. Bisulphites of potash, ammonia and other alkalies may be substituted for the bisulphite of soda, but the latter is to be preferred, because its preparation is cheaper, more easy, and better known.

PREPARATION OF BISULPHITE OF SODA FOR COLD SILVERING.

Put into a tall vessel of glass or porcelain, water, 10 pints ; crystalized carbonate of soda, 10 lbs. Pour a little mercury into the bottom of the vessel, so that the glass tube carrying sulphurous acid gas, which has to be placed into it, may not be stopped by the crystals formed during the operation. Arrange an apparatus for the production of sulphurous acid gas, and let the washed gas pass through the vessel holding the carbonate of soda. Part of the soda is transformed into sulphite of soda, which dissolves, and a part falls to the bottom as bicarbonate. The latter is, however, transformed into sulphite of soda by a continuous production of sulphurous acid, and the carbonate acid escapes. When all has dissolved, continue the passage of sulphurous acid until the liquid slightly reddens blue litmus pape , and then put the whole aside for 24 hours. After that time some crystals are found upon the mercury, and the liquid above, more or less colored, is the bisulphite of soda for silvering. The crystals are separated from the mercury, drained, and kept for gilding baths. They are not suitable for silvering.

The liquid bisulphite of soda thus prepared, should be stirred with a glass rod, to throw off the carbonic acid which may still remain. The liquor should then be again tried with blue litmus paper. If it turns a deep red, add a little carbonate of soda for neutralizing the excess of sulphurous acid ; if red litmus paper becomes blue, there is too much alkali, and more sulphurous acid gas should be passed through the liquid, which is in the best condition when litmus paper becomes violet or slightly red. This solution marks from 22° to 26° Baumé, and must not come in contact with iron, zinc, tin, or lead.

COLD SILVERING BATH FOR DIPPING.

A stoneware or glass vessel is about three parts filled with the liquid bisulphite of soda, a solution of nitrate of silver in distilled water, of medium concentration, is gradually added while the bath is continually stirred with a glass rod ; a white flocculent precipitate of sulphite of silver is produced by stirring ; this is dissolved by the bisulphite of soda. The silver solution is added so long as the precipitate readily disappears, and stopped when it becomes slow to dissolve. This bath is always ready to work, and instantaneously produces a magnificent silvering upon copper, bronze, or brass articles which have been thoroughly cleansed, and passed through a weak solution of nitrate of binoxide of mercury, although this last operation is not absolutely necessary. According to the length of time of the immersion the bath will give, a very fine whitening by silver is as cheap as any of the other described processes ; a bright silvering, especially adapted for setting jewelry ; or a silvering with a dead luster, still more durable, without electricity, and in the cold. The loss of silver is made good by additions of nitrate of silver. When the proportion of bisulphite is not sufficient to dissolve the metallic salt, add some bisulphite of soda to restore the bath to its primitive state. Silver is slowly deposited upon the sides of the vessel ; this may be dissolved in nitric acid for future uses.

SOLUTION OF SILVER OR GOLD FOR SILVERING OR GILDING WITHOUT THE AID OF A BATTERY.

1 oz. of nitrate of silver is dissolved in one quart of rain or distilled water, and a few crystals of hyposulphite of soda added,

which form a brown precipitate soluble in a slight excess of hyposulphite. Small articles of steel, brass, or German silver may be silvered by dipping a sponge in the solution and rubbing it over the surface of the article to be coated. A solution of chloride of gold may be treated in the same manner, and applied as described. A more concentrated solution of either gold or silver may be used for coating parts of articles which have stripped or blistered, by applying it with a camel-hair pencil to the part, and touching the spot at the same time with a thin clean strip of zinc.

SILVER ELECTRO-PLATING.

BATH FOR SILVER ELECTROPLATING.

Water, 2¼ galls. ; cyanide of potassium, pure, 17¼ oz. ; pure silver for cyanide, 8¾ oz. The composition of commercial cyanide of potassium is exceedingly irregular. The pure, or No. 1, contains from 90 to 100 per cent. of real cyanide, and is especially employed for gilding and silvering baths. No. 2 contains from 60 to 70 per cent. of real cyanide ; it is the article prepared by Liebig's method, and is used for electro-baths of copper and brass. No. 3, which marks from 55° to 60°, is for scouring and preparing baths.

1. Put in a porcelain dish, holding a quart, pure granulated silver, 8¾ oz. ; pure nitric acid at 40° Baumé, 17¼ oz. Heat by charcoal or gas. The dish should be supported by an iron triangle, and not in direct contact with the fire. The acid rapidly attacks and dissolves the silver with an abundant production of yellow nitrous vapors, which must not be inhaled. When the vapors have disappeared, there remains a liquid more or less colorless, according to the proportion of copper held by the commercial silver, which is seldom entirely pure. The heat is then increased in order to evaporate the excess of acid, which escapes in white fumes. The material in the dish swells up and dries, and, with a further increase of heat, melts like wax. The dish is then removed from the fire, and being held with a cloth, the molten mass is made to flow upon the sides, where it soon solidifies ; the fused nitrate of silver, (lunar caustic,) is more or less white or gray, according to the purity of the silver employed. When perfectly cooled, turn the dish upside down, and by a gentle tap on the sides, the mass is detached.

2. Dissolve the nitrate of silver in ten or fifteen times its weight of distilled water ; hydrocyanic acid poured into this solution immediately produces an abundant white precipitate of cyanide of

silver. A sufficient quantity of prussic acid has been employed when, by adding a few drops of it to the clear liquid, no precipitate or turbidity appears. Throw the liquid upon a filter of muslin stretched on a wooden frame, the cyanide of silver remains on the cloth, the solution with the nitric acid and excess of prussic acid passes through. Wash the precipitate left upon the filter two or three times with pure water.

3. This cyanide of silver is put into the vessel intended for the bath and stirred with the 2¼ galls. of water. The cyanide of potassium is then added, dissolves it, and also dissolves the cyanide of silver, thus giving a solution of a double cyanide of potassium and silver.

Those who employ small baths, often renovated, may substitute for the cyanide of silver the chloride, or the nitrate of this metal. In the latter case, the quantity of cyanide of potassium should be increased. Such baths will be prepared as follows :—

1. The nitrate of silver is prepared in the manner indicated above, and 5¼ oz. of it, nearly equal to 3½ oz. of pure silver, are dissolved in 2¼ galls. of water.

2. The cyanide of potassium No. 1, about 8¾ oz., is then added. Stir to facilitate the solution, filter the liquor, to separate the iron contained in the cyanide. This operation may in some cases be dispensed with, because the iron rapidly falls to the bottom of the bath, and the solution becomes limpid.

The proportion of cyanide of potassium employed is more than is required for dissolving the silver, as 1¼ parts of good cyanide is sufficient for one part of silver ; but unless there is an excess of cyanide of potassium, the liquors do not conduct electricity well, and the deposit of silver is granulated and irregular. The silvering is effected with a battery, and with baths either warm or cold. The latter method is generally adopted for articles which require great solidity. The hot process is used for small articles, and is preferable for steel, iron, zinc, lead, and tin which have been previously electro-coppered.

The hot baths are generally kept in enameled cast iron kettles, and the articles are either suspended, or moved constantly about in them. The preliminary cleansing in acids, and passing through the mercurial solution, are necessary. A somewhat energetic current is needed, especially when the articles are moved about, in order to operate rapidly. There is too much electricity when the articles connected with the negative pole of the battery become gray or black, and produce many bubbles of gas.

A platinum, large wire or thin foil anode, is generally preferred to the soluble anode of silver employed in cold baths, but the solution is rapidly impoverished. In hot silvering baths, the separate battery is often replaced by a zinc wire wrapped around the articles.

The points of contract of the two metals are black or gray, but the stain disappears by plunging the object into the liquor for a few moments, after it has been separated from the zinc, and carefully scratch-brushed.

Instead of separate batteries, a simple apparatus may be made of a glass, porcelain or stone-ware vessel holding the bath, and in the centre of which is a porous jar filled with a solution of 10 per cent. of cyanide of potassium or common salt. The cylinder of zinc, immersed in this porous jar, carries a larger circle of brass wire, the cross diameters of which are soldered to the zinc. This brass ring projects over the bath, and the articles, suspended to the ring by slinging wires, hang down into the bath. At the beginning, the operation goes on rapidly, and the deposit is good; but, after a time, the solution of zinc traverses the porous cell and impairs the purity of the bath.

An impoverished hot bath is reinvigorated by additions of equal parts of cyanide of potassium and silver salt. It is necessary to replace the water in proportion as it is evaporated. When the silver baths rapidly deposit metal without the aid of electricity, it is a proof that they are too rich in cyanide, or too poor in silver. A deposit affected under such conditions is rarely adhering, especially when upon articles previously coppered, because the excess of cyanide dissolves the deposited copper, and the silver which takes its place may be removed with the finger. The remedy consists in adding to the bath only enough silver salt and no more, so that a piece of copper will not become sensibly silvered in it, without the aid of electricity.

The cold electro-silvering baths generally employed for electroplating such articles as table-spoons or forks are contained in large rectangular wooden troughs lined with gutta-percha, or made of riveted wrought iron. They are sufficiently high to allow about 4 inches of liquid above the immersed object, whose distance from the bottom and sides should be nearly the same, to give a regular deposit of metal at both extremities of the object. The upper ledge of the trough carries two brass rods all round, which do not touch one another, one above the other, so that other metallic rods, being put across, will rest upon the higher or the lower rod, but not both at the same time. Each rod is connected with one of the poles of the battery by conducting wires, the points of contact of which should be perfectly clean. The rod which supports the articles to be silvered is connected with the negative pole represented by zinc in most batteries; and the other, supporting the anodes, is attached to the positive pole.

which is carbon with Bunsen's elements, copper for Daniell's, and platinum with Grove's cells.

A certain number of spoons and forks fixed to a rod, by means of copper wires, are cleansed at the same time, and the rod is placed upon the negative conducting rod of the trough. Then, facing these articles hang upon the positive conducting wire of the trough another metallic rod to which the soluble silver anode is attached like a flag. Next comes another series of spoons and forks, faced by another soluble anode, in such a manner that each row of spoons and forks is between two anodes. The articles to be silvered all rest upon the negative conducting rod, and the soluble anodes upon the positive one. This disposition is for obtaining an equal deposit upon all the pieces.

The objects require turning upside down during the operation, in order to prevent a thicker deposit on the lower parts, as the richest part of the solution is the densest, and therefore lies near the bottom of the trough. The denser layers, being richer in metal, deposit it more abundantly upon the direction which they follow, and form grooves which cannot be filled by the lighter and poorer currents. It is, therefore, advantageous to keep the objects in constant motion. In this case the frame supporting the articles does not rest upon the trough, but is suspended above the bath, and receives its motion from a small eccentric, or other motive power. The silver deposit will adhere strongly, if the articles have been fully amalgamated in the solution of nitrate of binoxide of mercury, and have remained in the silver bath from 12 to 15 hours, according to the intensity of the current. The silvering will be the better and finer as the intensity of the current is weaker, up to a certain limit. A sufficient quantity of silver may be deposited in 3 or 4 hours, but the result is not satisfactory, and the burnishing is very difficult.

When the articles have acquired a film of silver, they are sometimes removed from the bath and thoroughly scratch-brushed, cleansed in alcohol, or, preferably, in a hot silvering bath, thence again passed through the mercurial solution, and finished in the former cold electro bath. This first scratch-brushing, which is not always necessary, obviates the tendency of certain alloys to assume a crystalline appearance, and corrects imperfections of the cleansing process.

Electro-silvering baths do not generally work so well when freshly prepared, as when they have been used for a certain time ; the deposit is often granulated, bluish, or yellowish. It is, therefore, desirable to mix a portion of old liquors with those recently prepared, or new baths may acquire an artificial age by boiling a few hours, or adding one or two thousandths of aqua ammonia.

TO ELECTROPLATE OVER SOLDER.

Cleanse from grease with caustic potash. Dip quickly in red nitrous acid, in order to remove oxide, and then wash away with water all traces of acid. Make a solution of mercury in cyanide of potassium; into this dip the joint for a short time; then wash in water as before. The silver may be then easily deposited upon the amalgamated surface.

TO PREVENT ELECTRO-SILVER PLATING TURNING YELLOW BY CONTACT WITH THE AIR.

This change of color is due to the deposit, by galvanic action, of pure silver and of a subsalt, the subcyanide of silver, which is rapidly decomposed and darkened by light. It is therefore neces- sary to remove the subcyanide by one of the following methods:

1. The articles are left immersed in the bath for some time after the electric current has been interrupted, when the subcyanide of silver is dissolved by the cyanide of potassium.

2. Having smeared the objects with a paste of borax, they are heated in a muffle until the salt fuses and dissolves the sub- cyanide. This process anneals and softens the metal.

3. The poles of the battery are inverted for a few seconds, that is to say, the articles become soluble anodes, and the electric current carries away the subcyanide of silver in preference to the metal; this operation should be very short, otherwise the silver will entirely abandon the objects and will coat the silver sheets.

SILVER-PLATING BRITANNIA METAL, PEWTER, AND ALL COMBI- NATIONS OF LEAD AND TIN.

These are best placed in a solution containing a good deal of free cyanide, and the deposit should be rapid at first. The sur- face of the anode should be about three times that required for German silver and the battery power strong, but not too intense. It is better not to disturb these articles in the solution at the be- ginning of the deposit. Afterward they may be shifted for ob- taining a uniform coat. If the articles, when they have been a short time in the plating bath, present an unequal surface, re- move them, and brush over again as before; then, after well rinsing, return quickly to the bath and allow them, if possible, to remain without further disturbance.

SMALL SILVER BATH FOR AMATEURS.

The bath is a cylindrical stoneware, glass, or porcelain vessel. After cleansing and amalgamation, the articles are attached by clean copper wires to the circumference of a brass ring, supported upon the top of the apparatus by three or four soldered cross-wires. The ring is connected with the negative pole of the battery, and the positive pole with a platinum anode, or a cylinder formed of a sheet of silver rolled round, which dips into the middle of the apparatus. The articles must be now and then turned upside down, and sideways, so that each face of the object will be, in turn, directly opposite the silver anode, and thus also the points of contact with the suspending wires receive their quota of metallic deposit. Points, edges, corners, and all raised parts, offer a more easy passage to the electric current, and therefore become more coated with metal. As the wear of tablespoons and forks is greater on their convex sides, those parts should face the silver anode longer than the concave portions.

BRIGHT LUSTER.

Bisulphide of carbon, in small proportion, imparts a bright luster to electroplated articles. Put an ounce of bisulphide of carbon into a pint bottle containing a strong silver solution with cyanide in excess. The bottle should be repeatedly shaken, and the mixture is ready for use in a few days. A few drops of this solution may be poured into the plating bath occasionally, until the work appears sufficiently bright. The bisulphide solution, however, must be added with care, for an excess is apt to spoil the solution. In plating surfaces which cannot easily be scratch-brushed, this brightening process is very serviceable. Care must be taken never to add too much at a time.

DEPOSITS ON SOLDER.

The difficulty of obtaining regular deposits of gold or silver over articles which have parts soldered may be greatly obviated by scratch-brushing those parts dry, that is, without the usual liquid employed. This renders these refractory parts better conducting, provided that during the operation no impurities are left on these spots.

METHOD BY WHICH THE WEIGHT OF DEPOSITED SILVER IS DIRECTLY ASCERTAINED.

1. The articles are cleansed by the processes already described, then dried saw-dust or otherwise, and weighed in a scale. However rapidly this may be done the surface of the copper will be slightly oxidized and tarnished ; to recover their former cleanliness the articles must be plunged into a strong pickel of sulphuric acid, and then into the mercurial solution. After rinsing, and immersion in the bath, practical experience will teach when it is nearly time to withdraw the articles from the solution. They

will have to be wighed several times before the intended weight of silver has been deposited.

2. Cleanse the articles, and put them immediately into the bath, except one, which is treated as above, and used as a test. This piece is now and then removed from the bath to ascertain its increase of weight, and when it has acquired its proportion of silver it is supposed the other pieces are also finished. Strongly amalgamated articles will not become sensibly oxidized during the drying which precedes their weighing. When the objects have been dried in order to ascertain the proportion of deposited silver, they should not be returned to the bath without having been cleaned in a hot solution of cyanide of potassium, which dissolves the grease from handling, and passed again through the solution of nitrate of binoxide of mercury, and rinsed. Alcohol may be substituted for the hot solution of cyanide, but the results are not so sure, and the expense is greater. Both these methods are tedious, and only give approximate results.

3. Remove one dish of an ordinary pair of scales substitute for it a metallic frame which supports the articles to be silvered, and communicates through the beam and the column with the negative electrode of a battery ; connect the soluble anode with the positive pole. When the articles are suspended to the frame, and are in the bath, the equilibrium of the scale is established by weights upon the other dish ; add to this a weight equal to the silver it is desired to deposit. The operation will be finished when the equilibrium of the beam is re-established. This method is not mathematically accurate, but is sufficiently exact for all practical purposes. An automatic arrangement, by which the electric current may be broken at the time the articles in the bath have received a sufficient deposit of silver, is easily arranged, and saves time and metal.

ANODES.

Should the anodes become black during the passage of the electric current, the solution contains too little cyanide of potassium and too much silver. In this case the deposit is adherent, but too slow, and the bath loses more silver than it can gain from the anodes. Carefully add sufficient cyanide of potassium. If the anodes remain white during the current, the proportion of cyanide of potassium is too great, the deposited silver is often without adherence, and the anodes lose more metal than is deposited ; add silver salt until it dissolves with difficulty. When in good working order the soluble anodes become grey during the passage of the electricity, and white when the circuit is broken. The specific gravity of the bath may vary from 5° to 15° of the Baumé hydrometer for salts, and still furnish good results.

There is a simple and rapid process for ascertaining the state of the bath, and establishing the proper ratio between the silver and the cyanide. About half a pint of the liquor is put into a tall glass, and a solution of one-third of an ounce of nitrate of silver in 3 oz. of distilled water is poured into the former, drop by drop. If the white precipitate produced is rapidly dissolved by stirring, the liquor is too rich in cyanide, or too poor in silver ; should the precipitate remain undissolved after long stirring, the liquor is too rich in silver or too poor in cyanide of potassium. When the precipitate is dissolved but slowly, the liquor is in the best condition.

BURNISHING.

By burnishing, the roughness of an object is flattened down until the surface is smooth and polished, like a looking-glass. Burnishing is an important operation for electro-deposits which consist of a multitude of small crystals with intervals between them, and with facets reflecting the light in every direction. The deposited metal is hardened, and forced into the pores of the underlaying metal, and the durability is thus increased to such an extent, that with the same amount of silver a burnished article will last twice as long as one which has not been so treated. The instruments employed for burnishing are made of different materials, and must be of great hardness and a perfect polish. Such are hardened cast steel, agate, flint, and blood-stone.

For metallic electro-deposits steel and blood-stones are especially employed. There are several qualities of blood-stone ; its grain should be close, hard and without seams or veins ; it should leave no white lines on the burnished parts, nor take off any metal, and its color should be of an intense black-red. The steel must be fine and close grained, and perfectly polished. Should the polish of any burnishing tool alter by use, it is restored by friction upon a skin or leather attached to a wooden block, which is fixed to the bench. The leather is covered with polishing rouge in impalpable powder, or, preferably, with pure alumina obtained by calcining ammonia alum in a forge fire. Venetian tripoli, rotten-stone, tin putty, emery, or many other hard substances finely powdered may be employed.

The burnishing tools are of various shapes, such as a lance, a tooth, a knife, a half-sphere, or a dog's tongue, and a considerable stock is necessary. The burnishing is divided into two distinct operations ; the first consists in roughing, and the second in finishing. The tools for the first have a sharp edge, whilst for the second operation they have a rounded surface. The tools for the hand or the lathe are fixed by copper ferules into the short round wooden handles, so that the hand is not influenced by their weight ; the tools for the arm or the vice are fastened to wooden handles sufficiently long to rest their slender part upon the arm or the shoulder, the stouter lower portion is grasped by the hand.

The burnishing tools and the objects must be frequently wetted by certain solutions, some of which facilitate the sliding of the instrument, or with others which have a chemical action upon the shade of the burnished articles. Of the first are pure water, solutions of soap, decoctions of linseed, and infusions of the roots of marsh-mallow or liquorice ; the second includes wine-lees, cream tartar, vinegar, alum in water. When burnishing gold applied upon electro-deposits of copper, as in gilding with a dead luster by that method, use pure water for fear of producing a disagreeable red shade. A solution of new soap is sometimes preferred by operators, although when old it imparts an unpleasant tinge, owing to the sulphides of the liquor. When the burnishing is completed, the surface is wiped longitudinally with a soft and old muslin rag.

The polish obtained by burnishing is called black, when it reflects the rays like a mirror ; and should the presence of mercury or a bad deposit prevent the tool from producing a bright surface, the object is said to be greasy. Articles which have been previously polished, and which generally receive a very trifling deposit, are not burnished, but rubbed with chamois leather and the best quality polishing-rouge. Too thick or too rapid electro-deposits cannot be burnished, but must be polished by rubbing with a leather and a mixture of oil and powdered pumice-stone, tripoli, or tin putty. Coarse powders are used at the beginning, and impalpable ones at the end of the operation. Polished silver deposits are more agreeable to the eye than burnished ones ; but the hardening of the latter renders them more durable.

TO DISSOLVE SILVER FROM SILVERED ARTICLES—COLD BATH.

For dissolving silver in the cold the objects are hung in a large vessel filled with the following mixture :—Sulphuric acid at 66° Baumé, 10 parts ; nitric acid at 40° Baumé, 1, in which they remain for a greater or less length of time, according to the thickness of the coat of silver to be dissolved. This liquid, when it does not contain water, dissolves the silver without sensibly corroding copper and its alloys ; therefore avoid introducing wet articles into it, and keep the liquid perfectly covered when not in use. As far as practicable place the articles in the liquid so as not to touch each other, and in a vertical position, so that the silver salt will fall to the bottom. In proportion as the action of the liquor diminishes, pour in small and gradual additions of nitric acid. Dissolving silver in the cold is regular and certain, but slow, especially when the proportion of silver is great. The other more rapid process is then resorted to.

HOT BATH.

Nearly fill a flat pan of enameled cast iron with concentrated sulphuric acid, and heat to a temperature of 300° to 400° Fahr.; at the moment of using it, pinches of dry powdered saltpeter are thrown into it; then hold the article with copper tongs in the liquid. The silver rapidly dissolves, and the copper or its alloys are not sensibly corroded. According to the rapidity of the solution more or fewer pinches of saltpeter are added. All the silver has been dissolved when, after rinsing in water and dipping the articles in the cleansing acids, they present no brown or black spots, that is, when they appear like new metals. These two methods are not suitable for removing the silver from wrought and cast iron, zinc, or lead; it is preferable to invert the electric current in a cyanide bath, or to use mechanical processes. Old desilvering liquors become green after use; to recover the silver they are diluted with four or five times their volume of water, then add hydrochloric acid or common salt. The precipitation is complete when the settled liquor does not become turbid by a new addition of common salt or hydrochloric acid. The resulting chloride of silver is separated from the liquid either by decantation or filtration, and is afterwards reduced to the metallic state by one of the methods which will be described.

RESISTS AND RESERVES.

By reserves, certain parts of a metallic article, which may be already covered with an electro-deposit on its whole surface, are coated with another metal. To gild the parts in relief of an object of which the body is silvered, make a gold reserve, and use a silver reserve for silvering of certain parts of a body already gilt. This requires a little practice and care, and a firm hand to make thin lines with the hair pencil. Thoroughly scratch-brush and wipe the object; the parts intended to have the primitive color must be covered by a brush with a resist varnish; dry in the air, or in a stove, or upon a gentle fire until it no longer feels sticky. Place in the bath; the galvanic deposit will only coat those parts unprotected by the varnish. The temperature of the bath should be low, and the current weak, for fear of having rough lines where the deposit touches the varnish, from the latter becoming softened, or from bubbles which are disengaged at the negative pole under the action of a strong electric current.

When the deposit is completed, remove the resist varnish with warm spirits of turpentine, and afterwards with tepid alcohol; naptha or benzole are preferable, as they rapidly dissolve in the cold nearly all resinous and fatty bodies, or the varnish may be destroyed by a brief immersion in concentrated sulphuric acid when cold. It often happens that several colors and metals have to be placed upon the same object, such as silver with both bright and a dead luster, and yellow, green, red, white, or pink golds, or platinum. Varnishes are also employed for avoiding the deposit of the precious metals upon those parts which do not need them.

RESIST OR RESERVE VARNISHES.

Dissolve in boiled linseed oil or spirits of turpentine, resin, or copal; these varnishes are not sufficiently colored to distinguish the places where they have been laid on, mix with them therefore a certain proportion of red-lead, chrome yellow, or Prussian blue, which at the same time facilitates their drying.

OLD SILVERING.

To imitate old artistic productions made of solid silver, the groundwork and hollow portions not subject to friction are covered with a blackish red earthy coat, the parts in relief remain with a bright lead luster. Mix a thin paste of finely-powdered plumbago with spirits of turpentine, to which a small proportion of red ochre may be added to imitate the copper tinge of certain old silverware; smear this all over the articles. After drying, gently rub with a soft brush, and the reliefs are set off by cleaning with a rag dipped in spirits of wine. Old silver is easily removed, and the brightness of the metal restored, by a hot solution of caustic potash, cyanide of potassium, or benzole. To give the old silver book to small articles, such as buttons and rings, throw them into the above paste, rub in a bag with a large quantity of common dry saw-dust until the desired shade is obtained.

OXIDIZED SILVER.

This is not an oxidization, but a combination with sulphur or chlorine. Sulphur, soluble sulphides, and hydrosulphuric acid blacken silver, and insoluble silver salts, and particularly the chloride of silver, rapidly blackens by solar light. Add four or five thousandths of hydrosulphate of ammonia, or of quintisulphide of potassium, to ordinary water at a temperature of 160° to 180° Fahr. When the articles are dipped into this solution an iridescent coating of silver sulphide covers them, which after a few seconds more in the liquid turns blue-black. Remove, rinse, scratch-brush, and burnish when desired. Use the solution when freshly prepared, or the prolonged heat will precipitate too much sulphur, and the deposit will be wanting in adherence ; besides the oxidization obtained in freshly-prepared liquors is always brighter and blacker than that produced in old solutions, which is dull and gray. If the coat of silver is too thin, and the liquor too strong, the alkaline sulphide dissolves the silver, and the underlaying metal appears. In this case cleanse and silver again, and use a weaker blackening solution.

Oxidized parts and gilding may be put upon the same article by the following methods : After the whole surface has been gilt, certain portions are covered with the resist varnish ; silver the remainder. Should the process of silvering by paste and cold rubbing be employed, the gilding should be very pale, because it is not preserved, and deeply reddened by the sulphur liquor. When this inconvenience occurs from a too concentrated liquor, it is partly remedied by rapidly washing the article in a tepid solution of cyanide of potassium.

Deep black is thus obtained upon cleansed copper ;—Dissolve 3 or 4 oz. of blue ashes, (hydrocarbonate of copper), in sufficient quantity of aqua ammonia, place the cleansed copper in this solution, cold or tepid, it will be instantaneously covered with a fine black deposit. This coat is so thin that burnished articles look like varnished black.

NIELLED SILVER.

This is a kind of inlaid enamel work, and is obtained by the sulphuration of certain parts of a silver object. But instead of being direct, this is produced by inlaying the silver surface with a sulphide of the same metal prepared beforehand. For preparing the niel, heat a certain proportion of sulphur in a deep crucible ; heat a certain quantity of silver, copper and lead in another crucible, and when melted pour into the fused sulphur, which transforms these metals into sulphides ; then add a little sal ammoniac, remove from the crucible and pulverize for use.

First crucible—flowers of sulphur, 27 oz. ; sal ammoniac, 2¾ oz.

Second crucible, which after fusion is poured into the first—silver, 1½ oz. ; copper, 1½ oz ; lead 2¾ oz.

1. After having reduced the niel to a fine powder, mix with a small proportion of a solution of sal ammoniac, hollow out the engraving upon a silver surface, and cover the whole, hollows and reliefs, with the composition. The article is then to be heated in a muffle until the composition solders to the metal. Uncover the pattern by a level polish, when the silver will appear as over a black ground. This method is costly, as each article must be engraved.

2. Engrave in relief a steel plate, and press it against the silver plate between two hard bodies. The copy is hollow, and ready to receive the niel. A great many copies may be obtained from the same matrix.

SILVERING LOOKING-GLASSES.

The metal used is quicksilver. The substance employed to make the mercury or quicksilver adhere to the surface of the glass is tin-foil, as thin as paper, and which has a strong attraction for mercury. A drop of mercury combines with the tin-foil, and they become as one substance, which adheres pretty firmly to glass The glass to be silvered is made perfectly clean on both sides, particularly on that which is to be silvered. If the slightest speck of dirt be allowed to remain on the surface, it will appear very conspicious when the glass is silvered. The tin-foil is generally made in sheets about 6 ft. long and of various widths, varying from 19 in. up to 40, the diversity of widths being to enable the silverer to cut out small pieces suitable to various-sized glasses. For larger sizes, the foil is generally made to order, and of a greater thickness than for smaller glasses. A sheet of tin-foil being unrolled, is laid down flat, and cut to the same shape as the glass, but an inch larger each way. It is then laid down as smoothly as possible on the silvering stone, which is a very large and carefully prepared slab of slate, porphyry, or marble, perfectly flat and smooth.

The foil is worked out level and smooth on the silvering stone by means of a smooth wooden roller, which is worked over it in every direction. The silverer pours some mercury into a wooden bowl, and then, by means of an iron ladel, pours the mercury over the whole surface of the foil till every part is covered. The glass plate is then laid upon the liquid mercury ; but it is not laid at once flat down on it, being made to slide on the edge of the glass first coming in contact with the mercury. As it is slid along, it pushes before it the greater part of the mercury, because the edge of the glass almost scrapes along the foil as it passes, that al. air-bubbles and impurities may be pushed off, allowing only a thin film of very pure mercury to remain between the glass and the foil. In this much care and delicacy are required.

It is a matter of considerable difficulty to clean the glass so perfectly as not to show any marks or streaks after it is silvered. It is often necessary to remove it from the foil two or three times after it has been laid down, to wipe off specks of dirt which are visible when the glass is silvered, however difficult of detection they may previously be ; this is especially the case in damp weather. This renders it necessary that the foils for large glasses, which necessarily require a longer time than small ones to perform the different processes, should be thicker than those for smaller ; for such is the attraction between the mercury and the foil, that if a glass after having been removed for further cleaning, is not speedily replaced on the mercury, the latter will combine with the foil, and give it a rottenness which will prevent its adhesion to the glass ; the thicker the foil, the less likely is this to occur.

When the glass is properly placed on the tin-foil, and it is ascertained that all specks and air-bubbles are removed, it is covered almost in every part by heavy iron or leaden weights ; so that a large glass will have several hundredweight pressing upon it. This pressure is to force out from between the glass and the foil as much mercury as possible, so that the thinnest film only shall remain between them. To effect this more completely, the silvering stone is made to rest on a swivel, underneath, by which it can be made either perfectly horizontal, or thrown into an inclined position. While the glass is being laid on the foil, the silvering stone is horizontal, to prevent the mercury from flowing off ; but when the superfluous mercury is to be drained off, the stone is made to assume an inclined position, so as to ensure one general direction for the flow of the mercury.

A hollow groove runs round the sides of the stone, into which the mercury flows as it is forced out from between the glass and the foil. A pipe, descending from one corner of this trough, conveys the mercury into a bottle placed beneath to receive it. Although an immense weight of mercury must be poured on the foil for the silvering of a large glass, yet the quantity which actually remains between the glass and the foil is extremely small. The glass, with the weights upon it, is allowed to remain in the inclined position for several hours, or, if the glass is large, it is allowed to remain until the next day, in order that as much as possible of the mercury may be pressed out before the weights are removed.

On the removal of the weights, one end of the glass is tilted up and supported by the blocks, the other end still remaining on the stone. A piece of foil is then laid on the lowest corner, to draw off the mercury which collects in a little pool at the bottom of the glass. In this state the glass remains from a few hours to 3 or 4 days, according to its size. When as much of the mercury as possible has drained from the glass in this way, the glass is taken up, when it is found that the two metals have combined together, and in the combined state adhere to the glass, which neither the one nor the other would have done separately. The removal of the glass from the stone is effected in three different ways, according to its size. If it is not too wide for the arm-span of the silverer, he takes it by the two edges, lifts it from the stone, and places it edgeways on the shelf or on the floor of the silvering room, resting its upper edge against the wall, and allowing one corner to be lower than the rest, so as to facilitate the draining toward that corner. If the glass is long and narrow, two men take it up instead of one, but in the same manner. If however, the glass is very large, the following mode is sometimes adopted.

The draining room, and an opening in the floor of the latter is so arranged that a portion of the silvering table can be let down through it, on account of its facility of motion round the swivel. By a gradual turning of the silvering table, the stone and the glass upon it can be brought into a nearly perpendicular position. In this position of the glass, several men in the lower room grasp it by the edges, and place it against the wall of the room, where it is left to drain. When the plate is thus placed against the wall of the room, it is left to drain for a time, varying from one day to several days, according to its size, in order that any remaining superfluous mercury may become still better attached to the surface of the glass. When the draining appears to be complete, the glass is ready to be applied to its intended purpose. The above is the process for silvering plate glass. But there is an important reason why common glass, used for cheaper purposes, such as the inferior sort of dressing-glasses, cannot be silvered in this way ; for any heavy pressure on such glass breaks it at once, on account of its thinness and crookedness. These common glasses, which are always small in size, are not silvered on a stone, but on a board or flat box. The foil is cut to the requisite size, and laid on the board and covered with mercury, as in the former instance.

But instead of sliding the glass on the mercury, a piece of clean paper is laid on the mercury, and the glass is laid on the paper. The silverer now, laying one hand pretty firmly on the glass, takes hold of the edge of the paper with the other, and by a quick motion, draws out the paper from between the glass and the foil, and with it the greater part of the mercury, together with air-bubbles and impurities,—leaving the glass resting on a thin but brilliant film of mercury ; this is a process requiring manual dexterity.

The common glass employed for these purposes is always irregularly bent at its surfaces ; it is a general rule to silver the concave side, when one side is more concave than the other. The crown glass now made is better that that which was produced a few years ago, and although it is always curved, yet the curvature is pretty nearly the same in different tables from the same crate. This circumstance assists the silverer, for each silvered glass acts as a weight to another of the same size. It is usual to silver a great number of the same size at the same time ; and as each one is silvered, it is placed flat down on a shelf, or in a shallow box ; and on it the others are successively laid as they are silvered. The concave side of each is silvered, and as the concavity is nearly equal in all, each one helps to press out the superfluous mercury from the one beneath it. The silvering in common glasses is seldom found to be so perfect as on plate glass, from the impossibility of giving equal pressure in every part.

SILVERING BY PRECIPITATION.

Place a sheet of glass, previously washed clean with water, on a table, and rub the whole surface with a rubber of cotton, wetted with distilled water, and afterward with a solution of Rochelle salts in distilled water, 1 of salt to 200 of water. Then take a solution, previously prepared by adding nitrate of silver to ammonia of commerce ; the silver being gradually added until a brown precipitate commences to be produced ; the solution is then filtered. For each square yard of glass take as much of the above solution as contains 20 grammes, about 300 grains, of silver, and to this add as much of a solution as contains 14 grammes of salt, and the strength of the latter solution should be so adjusted to that of the silver solution that the total weight of the mixture above mentioned may be 60 grammes. In a minute or two after the mixture is made it becomes turbid, and it is then immediately to be poured over the surface of the glass, which has previously been placed on a perfectly horizontal table, but the plate is blocked up at one end, to give it an inclination about 1 in 40 ; the liquid is then poured on in such a manner as to distribute it over the whole surface without allowing it to escape at the edges. When this is effected, the plate is placed in a horizontal position at a temperature of about 68° Fahr.

The silver will begin to appear in about 2 minutes, and in about 20 or 30 minutes sufficient silver will be deposited. The mixture is then poured off the plate, and the silver it contains afterward recovered. The surface is then washed four or five times, and the plate set up to dry. When dry, the plate is varnished, by pouring over it a varnish composed of gum dammar, 20 parts ; asphalt of bitumen, 5 ; gutta-percha, 5 ; and benzine, 85. This varnish will set hard on the glass, and the plate is then ready for use.

PARTIALLY RESILVERING PIER GLASS.

Remove the silvering from the injured part, clean the glass, form a wall of beeswax round the spot, pour on it some nitrate of silver, and precipitate the silver by sugar, or oil of cloves and spirits of wine. This does not leave a white mark round the prepared place.

SILVERING CURVED GLASS.

This is a French process, used not only for flat surfaces, but also for those which are curved, or cut into patterns. Dissolve 600 grains of neutral nitrate of silver in 1200 grains of distilled water, add 75 drops of a solution composed of 25 parts of distilled water, 10 of sesquicarbonete of ammonia, and 10 of ammonia, sp. gr., .980 ; add also 30 grains of ammonia, same sp. gr., and 1800 grains of alcohol sp. gr. .85. When clear, the liquor is decanted or filtered, and mixture of equal parts of alcohol and oil of cassia added to the silver solution in the proportion of 1 of the essence of cassia to 15 of the silver solution ; the mixture is agitated and left to settle, then filtered. Before pouring upon the glass surface or into the glass vessel to be silvered, the solution is mixed with 1-78th of its bulk of essence of cloves, (1 part oil of cloves, 3 parts alcohol.) The glass is thoroughly cleaned, and the silver solution applied and warmed to 100° Fahr. for about 3 hours ; the liquid is poured off, and the silver deposit washed, dried, and varnished.

SILVERING GLASS—DRAYTON'S PROCESS.

A mixture is made of 1 oz. of coarsely pulverized nitrate of silver, ¼ oz. spirits of hartshorn, and 2 oz. of water ; which, after standing for 24 hours, is filtered, the deposit upon the filter, which is silver, being preserved, and an addition is made thereto of 3 oz. of spirits of wine, at 60° above proof, or naphtha ; from 20 to 30 drops of oil of cassia are then added ; and, after remaining for about 6 hours longer, the solution is ready for use. The glass to be silvered with this solution must have a clean and polished surface ; it is to be placed in a horizontal position, and a wall of putty or other suitable material formed around it, so that the solution may cover the surface of the glass to the depth of from one-eighth to one-fourth of an inch.

After the solution has been poured on the glass, from 6 to 12 drops of a mixture of oil of cloves and spirits of wine, in the proportion of 1 part, by measure, of oil of cloves to 3 of spirits of wine, are dropped into it, at different places ; or the diluted oil of cloves may be mixed with the solution before it is poured upon the glass ; the more oil of cloves used, the more rapid will be the deposition of the silver ; but the operation should occupy about 2 hours.

When the required deposit has been obtained, the solution is

poured off ; and as soon as the silver on the glass is perfectly dry,
it is varnished with a composition formed by melting together
equal quantities of beeswax and tallow. The solution, after being
poured off, is allowed to stand for 3 or 4 days, in a close vessel,
as it still contains silver, and may be again employed after filtration, and the addition of a sufficient quantity of fresh ingredients
to supply the place of those which have been used. About 18
grains of nitrate of silver are used for each square foot of glass ,
but the quantity of spirit varies somewhat, as its evaporation depends upon the temperature of the atmosphere, and the duration
of the process. By the addition of a small quantity of oil of car-
raway or thyme, the color of the silver may be varied. The oil
of cassia of different manufacturers varies, so on its being mixed
with the solution it must be filtered previous to use.

SILVERING LARGE MIRRORS FOR PHOTOGRAPHY.

Dissolve 150 grains of nitrate of silver in 6 oz. of distilled water,
and to this add ammonia, drop by drop, until the precipitate at
first thrown down is redissolved. Now, having made a solution
of caustic potash, in the proportion of 2¼ oz. of the potash to 50
oz. of water, add 15 oz. of this to the above solution of silver ;
and add ammonia as before, until the deep-brown precipitate again
thrown down is redissolved. Now add 29 oz. of distilled water,
after which allow some solution of silver to be dropped in, gently
stirring all the while with a glass rod, until a precipitate begins to be
formed. Previous to the immersion of the glass to be silvered,
dissolve 1 oz. of sugar of milk in 10 oz. of water. This must be
filtered and kept in a separate bottle. Have ready a clean glass
vessel of a size sufficient to contain the glass plate to be silvered ;
when everything is ready, mix together the silver solution with
that of the sugar of milk, in the proportion of 10 of the former to
1 of the latter. Lower the glass down in the solution until it is
a little distance from the bottom, and allow it to remain there for
a period of time, varying from 15 to 4 hours, according to the
thickness of the coating of silver desired.

After removing it from the bath, wash with distilled water,
and, when dry, polish by means of a soft pad of cotton-velvet
charged with rouge. An intensely brilliant surface may be thus
obtained on both sides of the glass plate. Make a 3-grain solution
of ammonio-nitrate of silver. Render it slightly turbid by excess
of nitrate of silver, and then filter it. Just before using it add to
each ounce of the foregoing solution 2½ grains of Rochelle salt,
immerse the glass as before, and expose to a subdued light while
it remains in the bath. In about 2 hours the deposit of silver will
be sufficiently thick.

TO SILVER GLASS SPECULA.

Prepare three standard solutions. Solution A—Crystals of nitrate of silver, 90 grains ; distilled water, 4 oz. ; dissolve. Solution B—Potassa, pure by alcohol, 1 oz. ; distilled water, 25 oz. ; dissolve. Solution C—Milk-sugar, in powder, ½ oz. ; distilled water, 5 oz   Solutions A and B will keep in stoppered bottles for any length of time ; solution C must be fresh.

THE SILVERING FLUID.

To prepare sufficient for silvering an 8-in. speculum, pour 2 oz. of solution A into a glass vessel capable of holding 35 oz. Add, drop by drop, stirring all the time with a glass rod, as much liquid ammonia as is just necessary to obtain a clear solution of the gray precipitate first thrown down. Add 4 oz. of solution B. The brown-black precipitate formed must be just redissolved by the addition of more ammonia, as before. Add distilled water, until the bulk reaches 15 oz. and add, drop by drop, some of solution A, until a gray precipitate, which does not redissolve after stirring for three minutes, is obtained then add 15 oz. more of distilled water. Set this solution aside to settle. Do not filter. When all is ready for immersing the mirror, add to the silvering solution 2 oz. of solution C, and stir gently and thoroughly. Solution C may be filtered.

TO PREPARE THE SPECULUM.

Procure a circular block of wood, 2 inches thick, and 2 inches less in diameter than the speculum. Into this should be screwed three eye-pins, at equal distances. To these pins fasten stout whipcord, making a secure loop at the top. Melt some pitch in any convenient vessel, and, having placed the wooden block face upward, on a level table, pour on it the fluid pitch, and on the pitch place the back of the speculum, having previously moistened it with a little spirits of turpentine to secure adhesion. Let the whole rest until the pitch is cold.

TO CLEAN THE SPECULUM.

Place the speculum, cemented to the circular block, face upward, on a level table ; pour on it a small quantity of nitric acid, and rub it gently all over the surface with a brush made by plugging a brass tube with pure cotton-wood. Having perfectly cleaned the surface and sides, wash well with common water, and finally with distilled water. Place the speculum face downward, in a dish containing a little rectified spirits of wine, until the silvering fluid is ready.

SILVERING GLASS GLOBES.

1. Take ½ oz. of clean lead, and melt it with an equal weight of pure tin ; then immediately add ½ oz. of bismuth, and carefully skim off the dross ; remove the alloy from the fire, and before it grows cold add 5 oz. of mercury, and stir the whole well together ; then put the fluid amalgam into a clean glass and it is fit for use. When this amalgam is used for silvering, let it be first strained through a linen rag ; then gently pour some ounces thereof into the globe intended to be silvered ; the alloy should be poured into the globe by means of a paper or glass funnel reaching almost to the bottom of the globe, to prevent its splashing the sides ; the globe should be turned every way, very slowly, to fasten the silvering.

2. Make an alloy of 3 oz. of lead, 2 oz. of tin, and 5 oz. of bismuth ; put a portion of this alloy into the globe, and expose it to a gentle heat until the compound is melted ; it melts at 197° Fahr. ; then by turning the globe slowly round an equal coating may be laid on, which, when cold, hardens and firmly adheres. This is one of the cheapest and most durable methods of silvering glass globes internally.

3. Nitrate of silver, 1 oz. ; distilled water, 1 pint ; strong liquor ammonia, sufficient quantity, added very gradually, to first precipitate and then redissolve the silver ; then add honey, ¼ oz. Put sufficient quantity of this solution in the globe, and then place the globe in a saucepan of water ; boil it for 10 to 30 minutes, occasionally removing it to see the effect.

MISCELLANEOUS.

ANOTHER DIPPING BATH.

1. Take ¼ lb. of cyanide of potassium and ½ oz. of nitrate of silver ; dissolve all the cyanide in 16 oz. of distilled or boiled water, and the silver in a similar quantity in another vessel. Into the vessel containing the silver throw a spoonful of common salt ; stir this up well with a clean piece of wood and let it settle ; dissolve some salt in water, and after the silver solution is settled mix a few drops of the salt water in it. If there is any cloudiness formed it proves that all the silver is not thrown down, and more salt must be added, and then stir and allow to settle. If the addition of salt and water has no effect, the water may be decanted off, carefully preserving the white deposit. Now pour some boiling water on this deposit ; let it settle, and pour off as before. Do this at least three times ; pour off as dry as possible, and add about a pint of clean water, and then by ½ oz. at a

time, the cyanide solution, till all the white precipitate is dissolved; add enough water to make half a gallon. Stir well after each addition of cyanide solution.

If on dipping the article, which must be well cleaned with brick-dust and water, into this solution the silver deposits on immediately and in a dark powder, it must be weakened by adding more water; if it coats slowly, more white precipitate must be prepared, washed, and added to it. This must also be done when the solution is getting short of silver It works best at about 60 or 70 degrees of heat; a dry, warm room suits the operation.

Brass and copper only can be silvered; other metals require a battery. This method gives a beautiful result when the work is polished and burnished.

2. Clean the articles thoroughly, and then immerse them for a few seconds in a solution of cyanide of silver, which will plate them without any further trouble.

SILVERING FOR BAROMETER AND THERMOMETER SCALES.

Take ½ oz. of nitrate of silver; dissolve in half a teacupful of cold water; add ¼ lb. of cream of tartar, with 1½ lb. of common salt, beaten or ground fine. Mix and stir well together, adding water until it attains the consistence of a thick paste. Now lay the scale on a board, the brass or copper being previously well cleaned and cast off from fine sand-paper; rub the silvering on with your hand until it attains the appearance of silver, which will be a minute or so; now take the work off the board and rub a little wet whiting over it, wash out in clean cold water, and dry in saw-dust. If varnished with a thin coat of white hard varnish, reduced in spirits of wine, this will last for years. The above quantity of silvering used with care will silver six dozen brewers' thermometers, 14 inches long.

OXIDIZING SILVER ARTICLES.

Oxidize silver-plated articles by dissolving sulphate of copper, 2 dwts.; nitrate of potash, 1 dwt.; and muriate of ammonia, 2 dwts.; in a little acetic acid. Apply with a camel-hair pencil; but warm the article first, and expose the article to the fumes of sulphur in a closed box; the parts not to be colored must be coated with wax.

SILVERING POWDER.

Take 40 grains of silver dust; cream of tartar, 8 drams; common salt, 2; and 40 grains of powder of alum. Polish any silver articles with this powder and a soft leather.

SILVERING POWDER FOR COATING COPPER.

Nitrate of silver, 30 grains ; common salt, 20 ; cream of tartar, 3½ drams. Mix, moisten with water, and apply.

SILVERING CAST IRON.

Fifteen grammes of nitrate of silver are dissolved in 250 grammes of water, and 30 grammes of cyanide of potassium are added ; when the solution is complete, the liquid is poured into 750 grammes of water, in which 15 grammes of common salt have been previously dissolved. The cast iron intended to be silvered by this solution should, after having been well cleaned, be placed for a few minutes in a bath of nitric acid of 1.2 sp. gr., just previous to being placed in the silvering fluid.

PLATING PASTES.

1. Nitrate of silver, 1 part ; common salt, 1 ; cream of tartar, 7 ; powder and mix.

2. Nitrate of silver, 1 part ; cyanide of potassium, 3. Both are applied by wetting with a little water and rubbing on the article to be plated, which must be quite clean. Plating done by the above will be very thin, but it will be silver.

3. Get a glazed earthen vessel, put in 1 oz. of nitric acid, place it on a slow fire, it will boil instantly, and then throw in some pieces of real silver ; this will be dissolved at once. As soon as dissolved, throw in a good handful of common salt to kill the acid, then make into a paste with common whiting. The article required to be silvered to be cleaned from grease and dirt, and the paste to be applied with a little water and wash-leather. This paste will keep for years.

TO SEPARATE SILVER FROM COPPER.

Mix sulphuric acid, 1 part ; nitric acid, 1 ; water, 1 ; boil the metal in the mixture till it is dissolved, and throw in a little salt to cause the silver to subside.

TO BRIGHTEN TARNISHED JEWELRY.

First wash the articles in this cleansing solution :—Liquor potasæ, 1 fluid oz. ; water, 20 fluid oz. ; mix. Rinse them in cold or warm water, and then immerse them in the following gilders' pickle ;—Common salt, 1 part ; alum, 1 ; saltpeter, 2 ; water, 3 or 4 ; mix. Let them remain, stirring them now and then, until the surfaces assume a bright golden appearance. Five minutes at most will suffice, less time is generally required. Wash them again in cold or warm water, and dry them with chamois leather or in hot boxwood saw-dust.

FROSTED SILVER.

Dip the article in a solution of nitric acid and water, half and half, for a few minutes, then wash well in clean water and dry in hot saw-dust. When thoroughly dry brush the saw-dust away with a soft brush, and burnish the parts required to be bright.

SILVERING CLOCK DIALS.

Rub the dial with a mixture of chloride of silver, tartar, and sea-salt, and afterwards rub off the saline matter with water. This silvering is not durable, but it may be improved by heating the article, and repeating the operation, once, or oftener if thought necessary.

DESILVERING.

The following is a liquid which will dissolve silver without attacking copper, brass, or German silver, so as to remove the silver from silvered objects, plated ware, &c. It is a mixture of 1 part of nitric acid with 6 parts sulphuric, heated in a water-bath to 160° Fahr., at which temperature it operates best.

HARD-SOLDER PLATING.

Sheet silver is forced into a die, similar in shape to the article it is destined to cover, but of course only of one side of it; it is, therefore, necessary to repeat the process in order to produce a shell to fit the other side. Next, cut the edges of the shells level, and brush over the insides with a solution of water containing borax in excess, which has been boiled fifteen minutes, well stirring it with the brush every time it is used, and to anneal the shells by holding them over a clear fire until red hot, in the same manner as the sheet of silver was previously; then after slitting the edges by small scissor cuts about an eighth of an inch long, at intervals of about half an inch, lay the shells aside in a clean place, until the article is prepared to receive them, which is done by first heating it to a dull red heat in order to remove grease or rust; next carefully file the part on which the silver is to be fixed, using a medium cut file called a bastard, rubbing it occasionally with a piece of borax, and taking care not to handle the article with the fingers where filed, but to use pincers or tongs to shift it when required. Now, with the sharp point of a clean knife, carefully remove any granules of calcined borax found adhering to the inside of the shells, using the most extreme caution on this and on all other occasions to handle them on the outside only; and after lightly brushing the outside, to remove any dust

which may possibly be deposited there, adjust them on the article
(which should be first rubbed with borax all over) allowing the
edges of one shell to slightly overlap the edges of the other ; and,
supposing it to be a kidney link belonging to harness hames we
are hard soldering, cramp them on about every two inches with
very fine soft iron wire, about 24 or 25 gauge ; next wind loosely-
twisted twine, about five or six strands thick, very tightly over
all, putting the winds very close together, in fact it would be
better if they overlapped each other a little ; next fix in the
vise a small hard-wood block, and, holding the work on this,
thoroughly beat it all over, turning it about frequently, so that
every part may be equally beaten ; the tool used for this purpose
is called a madge, and is a lead hammer about three pounds in
weight, with the face covered with six or seven thicknesses of
stout woolen ; the object of this beating is to cause the silver
shells to grip the article very closely.   The solder, which is supplied to the operative in thin sheets, must now be well scoured
with emery cloth, brushed over with the borax solution, and
annealed in the same manner as the silver sheets ; cut it into
strips rather less than an eighth of an inch wide, and bind it into
the work all along those parts where the edges of the shells meet,
by winding over with fine iron wire the same size, or a little finer,
than that used for the cramping ; take the cramps off one by one
as the winding progress.   When adjusting the solder on ready for
binding, take notice to lay it on the shell that has its edge overlapped with the other shell, and, in afterward putting the work
into the fire, let it be in such a manner that what we may call the
underlapping shell is uppermost in the fire.

Next heat the work rather hotter than the hand can bear, and
thoroughly brush it over with the borax solution ; the heat immediately dries out the water, and leaves it covered with a thin
stratum of borax, but, as we do not require the borax all over,
take a dry hard brush and brush off a portion of it, leaving it only
on the overlapping shell edges and solder.

It will be seen from the foregoing that it is essential that the
silver should lie as closely to the work as possible, and that extreme care should be taken to keep the metals mechanically, and
by means of borax chemically, clean, and free from films of air
or oxide, which would prevent the junction of the metals by the
firing process, which next follows, being sound and good.

The first must be clear and bright, and be composed of coke or
charcoal in pieces of a uniform size ; this precaution is most
essential, as a regular heat cannot be otherwise insured.   Place
the work in the fire, heap some firing lightly and carefully on the
top of it, and bring it to a good red heat as possible by blowing

with bellows, taking extreme care to heat it equally all over, in order that all the solder may melt and flow equally at the time ; continue the heat for a few moments after the solder has flowed, then, taking the work from the fire, allow the solder to set, that is, to solidify, and quickly unwind the wire from off it, while it is still hot, otherwise the wire will be difficult to get off ; a coating of excessively hard fused borax will now be found adhering to the outside of the article, which can be removed by immersion in a strong solution of muriatic acid and water. The article, if a small one, is now virtually hard-solder plated, the remaining processes being simply to test the soundness, that is, the perfect adhesiveness of the silver coating, and the polishing off ; but if a large one, such as we are supposed to be plating, it is done in two portions, called by the workmen first end and last end, respectively, experience having shown that this method is most conducive to success—in fact, kidney links must of necessity be done so, the first end being done before the link is welded into the hame, and the last end afterward. Pole chains also have to be plated in separate links, one-half of a link only being done at one time, and, as they usually contain about thirty links, it follows that the whole process has to be repeated some sixty times for one pole chain, thus explaining why hard-solder plating pole chains is such a long and expensive job. Solder used in hard-solder silver plating usually contains about 7 parts of silver to 3 of brass.

The processes now being described assume that silver is the metal used to plate with, but they apply equally to other metals suitable for hard solder work, such as German silver and brass. A composite metal, termed gold-colored or gilding metal is occasionally hard soldered with, but it is very refractory in the working, as the proportion of alluminum it contains, although very small, renders it extremely hard and springy when rolled into sheets. Gold is rarely hard soldered with, mercurial gilding answering the same purpose.

The work having remained in the solution some 15 or 20 minutes, we now take it out, remove the borax, and dry it, and the next process tells if the former ones have been skillfully and cleanlily performed ; this is the hammering, and to execute it, take a small iron block about an inch square, by four or five inches long, fix it in the vise, and after lightly filing off the small projecting pieces of silver or solder, of which a few almost invariably occur in the firing, give the work a rub or two with emery cloth, and, laying it on the block, hammer it all over, with a flat-faced bright steel hammer, about six or eight ounces in weight ; this levels and hardens the silver, and shows if it is soundly fixed, because the moment an unsound place is struck with the hammer it rises up in a blister. Then comes a most troublesome and delicate job, for the blister must be filed off, and a patch put on in place of it, and when the work is fired a second time it is apt to rise (as the the technical term goes) in other places, and so the unskillful or unlucky workman has got into a mess from which he is fortunate if he escapes without sacrificing all his previous labor and materials. However, we have successfully surmounted all our difficulties, and find our work turn out sound, so will now take a smooth file and smooth the silver all over, and afterward rub it well with emery cloth to prepare it for the final polishing processes, which are effected by preparing finely-powdered pumice-stone, by mixing it with animal oil in such proportions that when squeezed in the hand it will be of just sufficient consistence to hold together ; next take a strip of buff leather, about an inch wide by a foot long, and glue or nail it tightly on a strip of wood about three-quarters of an inch thick, in such a manner that the buff leather projects an eighth of an inch over the edge of the wood—this is technically called a buff ; take a pinch of the prepared pumice, spread it on the buff, and rub the work with it all over, repeating the operation until all the file or other marks are rubbed out of it ; next, use a strip of woolen material moistened with a mixture of oil and powdered rotten-stone, using with all these three concluding processes a large quantity of what our forefathers termed elbow grease ; and now we have produced a sound and workman-like piece of hard-solder silver plating.

SOFT-SOLDER PLATING.

Hard-solder plating is preferred where there is very much wear and knocking about of the plated object. Soft-solder, or Close Plating, as it is generally called, answers very well for inside or top work—where there is little wear and few blows. It is called close plating probably because it is not liable to blistering during process but adheres easily and completely to the metal base. The following is the process :

The article being filed clean and smooth, and polished with emery cloth, is next well tinned by being dipped in a melted mixture of lead one part, and tin three parts. Give the objects tinned a smart jerk when lifted so as to leave an even coating of tin all over it, then lay the sheet silver upon the object, and giving it a blow with the "madge" obtain the shape of the object or the shape of the half of it to be plated at one time. Cut out the silver foil to the shape and then with a well-tinned copper bit rub the silver upon the object to be plated, beginning gently— holding the object and silver in a pair of tongs. The solder (tin covering the object) melts and holds the silver. The copper bit must be skillfully urged over the whole surface until the work is finished. If a blister rises cut it across (not out) let out the air and resolder with the bit and burnish it down. German silver and brass foil can be plated upon iron as well as silver by this process. The finishing is done in the same way as in hard-solder plating. Solder-plating of either kind is more lasting than that in which the foil is merely rubbed on a hot foundation of metal.

PICTURE FRAMING

AND

General Information for Picture Dealers.

It is oftentimes the case that both frames and oil paintings are left with the gilder to renovate, and it is highly important that he should be informed as to the best methods in use for cleaning, re-mounting, varnishing, &c., and also to know some of the best receipts used in the various processes. It may be as well to caution the inexperienced, not to attempt too much, as an error in judgment, or careless manipulation, may entirely ruin a valuable picture, and those who wish to undertake the restoration of oil paintings must, in the first place, be *careful*, and then try some of the most simple processes, before trying those which even tax the skill of the experienced.

The cleaning and restoration of paintings is usually paid for most liberally, and to the man of business, this chapter will be worth gold and silver, while the amateur who wishes to try his on one of his own pictures, will be delighted with his success, if he possesses the skill and judgment to follow the instructions laid down.

Oil paintings come to hand for restoration, in almost every stage of decay ; and where a valuable work of art has been neglected, with the canvass rotten, or worm eaten, or where the body of paint has parted from the canvass or where the picture is cracked badly, and pieces of the picture fell away ; it requires thought, judgment, and a careful and skillful man to treat these works of art, so that succeeding generations may be delighted with their beauty. We will begin by describing some of the more simple processes, in cleaning, repairing, varnishing, &c.

CLEANING.

Sometimes a painting simply requires cleaning, when a soft sponge used with soap and soft water, will accomplish all that is required.

CLEANING VARNISHED PICTURES.—There are conditions where the above simple process will not accomplish what is required ; where a thick coating of varnish has been applied to the picture and it has been hung in a smoky room, and dust and dirt has been allowed to gather and remain ; then it is that no high lights will be visible, the sky will be dirty, no distance visible, and perhaps the figures in the foreground, but very indistinct. Under these conditions the varnish must be either removed or the smoke and dirt must be brought out of the varnish. If it is thought desirable to try the latter, the following receipt will be found valuable for the purpose :—2 oz. wood naptha, 1 oz. muriatic acid, ¼ pint of linseed oil.

Mix the above well together, and before using shake the bottle. It can be used as follows :—Get some soft linen rags, and make up a soft pad, which place on the mouth of the bottle and shake up some of the mixture into the pad, then commence rubbing the picture with a circular motion, and when nearly dry give the pad another dressing of mixture, and continue this mode of procedure for some time, when the picture will gradually come out in all its detail.

Removing the varnish requires care that the picture is not damaged, and must be watched as you proceed, as follows:— With the third finger of the right hand commence rubbing the varnish in a circular form, when it will be found (if the picture has been varnished with the right kind of varnish) that a fine dust or powder begins to come off the picture, and will continue to rub off till the whole of the varnished surface has disappeared, and the surface of the picture can then be sponged.

LINING.

Old pictures in time require lining when the canvas is rotten, torn, or damaged, and if not repaired rapidly go to decay. A new stretcher and canvas is usually prepared the size required, when the picture is carefully cut from the old stretcher, and with thin glue (not too hot) cover the back of the picture, and lay it down on the new corners, taking care to lay it at first in its proper

place, as it would be impossible to raise it again without damage.
The picture must not lie in the glue too long.

BLISTERED PAINTINGS.

Oftentimes in old paintings the paint will become disengaged
from the priming of the canvas through damp and other causes
in blisters, and if not seen to is liable to get broken out of the
picture. A successful method employed has been to puncture
the blister with a pin in numerous holes, and then rub in some
good paste carefully, and when enough of the paste has been introduced the surface is scraped clean, and rubbed over with an
oil rag moistened with linseed oil. Cover the part with a white
sheet of paper, and pass over the spot a flat iron, not too hot,
when it will be found the detached part will be firmly adhering
to the canvas.

TO SMOOTH A DAMAGED PICTURE.

Paintings sometimes get convex and concave patches on their
surface, owing to pressure on one side or the other, and these
inequalities cause a great deal of trouble to bring out. The most
successful way is to well wet the picture both sides on the spot,
and keep it under pressure till dry. With small pictures the
quickest way would be to take them off the stretcher and lay
them in a press, with a light pressure between soft sheets of
paper.

VARNISHING.

Care should be taken that the best mastic varnish only should
be used, and laid on with a flat ground hog's hair tool in tin.
Pour on the center of the picture a supply of varnish, and commence at one edge and work over to the other side, and then repeat this operation from the other edges, so as to cross the varnish and get it laid evenly.

FIELDING ON RESTORATION OF OLD PAINTINGS.

The usual commencement is with soft water and common yellow soap, with soft soap and water, or with ox-gall and water ;
the latter being stronger than soaps. When these have been well
applied with a very soft sponge containing not the least particle of grit or sand, the picture is to be washed with clean water,
and made perfectly dry with old linen cloth or silk handker-
chiefs, the latter are preferable. In using the ox-gall the best
method would be to lay it on the picture (which is to be placed
horizontally) with a brush, and when the first layer is dry add
another afterward, allowing the gall to remain on the picture for

two or three days ; then with a sponge and a plentiful supply of clean water, it will be perceived that a considerable quantity of various impurities have attached themselves to the gall, and are removed at the same time with it, leaving the picture so considerably improved in appearance as sometimes to require little or nothing more. Before much water is used in the first stages of picture cleaning, the state of the painting must be considered, for if the color be much broken up, or cracked over the whole surface, it might be rather dangerous to apply much water in the first instance. In cases of this kind we recommend that the back of the picture be well saturated with copal varnish by several applications with a strong brush previous to its being lined. This will in a great measure assist in attaching the ground on which the picture has been painted to the cloth, and perhaps entirely prevent the tendency that grounds much broken into have to leave the cloth ; yet, when all has been done that can be, by varnishing the back, it will be still necessary to use no more water than is absolutely necessary, unless well assured that no size or glue has been used in the composition of the ground. If more be necessary after these washings, as the removal of the varnish, &c., use a little smart friction with the finger, dipped previously into a box of *impalpable* pumice-stone powders ; this will ascertain by the peculiar smell produced whether the varnish that has been used be mastic or not. If it be mastic, it may by a continuance of the same process, be rubbed off all the delicate parts of the picture without much risk of taking up the colors, as the varnish rises under the finger in the form of a white powder, which ceases to rise after the whole has been taken off. We must add, that after the varnish has begun to come off freely in powder, no more pumice-powder need be used.

TO REMOVE VARNISHES.

In removing varnishes of a recent date, pumice-stone powder may be employed, and a very soft and fine bottle cork will save the fingers, but nothing will answer so well as the finger on the more delicate tints, for the removal of a strong varnish, as copal, &c., a mixture of spirit of wine and spirit of turpentine will be required. To make these two spirits unite, a small quantity of salt of tartar (tartrate of potassa) is to be added. Every time this is used the bottle is to be well shaken, very little poured on the picture, and rubbed on with a small piece of flannel ; then lay on the part rubbed a few drops of olive oil to retard the action of the spirits. These operations are to be repeated over the whole picture, frequently changing the pieces of flannel, and as frequently applying the olive oil in order to see what progress has been made. The picture, lastly, is to be washed with a sponge, soap, and water, afterward with clean water and then covered with a fresh varnish. If any stains should be found on the picture so unconquerable as to remain after the above process, a little oil of spike lavander will certainly remove them ; but the greatest care must be taken in using this essential oil ; it softens old paint so quickly that there is scarcely time to apply it and the olive oil before it has gone too far ; it is better to reduce its strength with spirits of turpentine if it should happen to be too genuine. Many use lancets and small scrapers, but this operation has also its risks from scratches, &c.

ANOTHER METHOD.—Soluble varnishes (as sugar, glue, gum-arabic, honey, isinglass, and white of egg) and dirt generally may be removed with hot water. To ascertain whether the painting be coated or varnished with such materials, moisten some part with water and try if it is clammy to the touch. To clean the picture, lay it horizontally upon a table or some convenient stand, and go over the surface with a sponge dipped in boiling water, the process to be continued till the coating begins to soften, when the heat must be gradually lowered as the varnish is removed. If, however, the coating stubbornly adheres, gentle friction with stale bread crumbs, a damp linen cloth, or the end of the forefinger, will generally effect the object or assist in doing so. White of egg, if not coagulated, may be removed by heat, by using an excess of albumen and cold water; but if coagulated, by employing a weak solution of a caustic alkali, as potash. Coated dirt is removed by washing with warm water, then covering with spirit of wine, renewed for ten minutes, and washing off with water without rubbing. Spots or stains should be washed with water, dried with soft linen rags, and covered with olive oil, warmed ; after the oil has remained on for twenty minutes, gentle friction with the finger should be used, the foul oil wiped off, and fresh oil laid on until the spots disappear. Should this fail, spirits of wine, essence of lemon, or oil of turpentine, may be carefully applied, observing that the stained parts only are to be covered. These applications should be cleaned off, first with water, then with olive oil. Sometimes even these means fail ; in such cases strong soap suds should be applied to the spots and retained there until they disappear. The parts must then be washed with water. To restore an oil painting, clean the decayed picture thoroughly, and spread it, face downward, upon a smooth table ; well moisten the back with boiling water, and when the canvas is sufficiently moistened, turn the picture face upward, stretch it tightly and nail it down to the table all round the edges. Then cover the painting with very hot strong glue, and over this, nearly all round the border, linen cloth, somewhat worn, of the same size as the picture. The picture should then be exposed to the sun to dry as quickly as possible. When dry detach it from the table, and nail it down again face downward. Then place a slightly raised border of wax all round the edges, and placing the table on a perfect level, pour over the picture a mixture of nitric acid and water. Care must be taken that this mixture be not too strong this is ascertained by dipping the finger in it, and if the finger does not turn yellow immediately, the mixture is in due proportion. Suffer this fluid to remain upon the canvas till the texture is quite dissolved and the thread rotted ; then pour it off, and detach the threads of the canvas with a spatula ; thus, the crust of the painting will alone remain glued face downward to the linen cloth before mentioned. Then wash the crust with pure water, wipe it with a fine sponge and leave it to dry. When dry, cover it with glue, mixed with a little spirits of wine, coat a piece of new canvas about the size of the picture with this, and spread it smoothly, and press it upon the back of the picture. The pressure may be accelerated with plates of lead or marble slabs, these being cleaned from time to time of any particles of glue that may adhere to them. All that now remains to be done is to remove the linen cloth and glue from the face of the painting. As soon, therefore, as the last glueing is dry, detach the whole from the table, and turn the linen cloth up and moisten it with the mixture of aquafortis and water ; by this means its texture will soon be destroyed, and may be broken away, the glue being removed with hot water. The painting will then be transferred perfect and entire to a new canvas. When the painting is *on wood* the wood must be pared until it be very thin, and the mixture of aquafortis and water being poured upon the remaining portion, will speedily dissolve its texture, and render the picture easy of removal. This is a delicate process and requires great care and experience.

TORN CANVAS.

A torn canvas may be repaired by cutting a suitable sized piece of close canvas, and dipping it into melted wax, applying it hot at the back of the picture to be repaired. The torn part must be carefully brought together and smoothed down. As the wax chills the canvas adheres firmly, and the superfluous wax at the back and front of the picture must be taken off. When dry fill up the interstices with compo used by gilders, and it will be found that the paint will adhere readily.

It is not expected that any of the foregoing methods will restore the colors of old pictures, for in course of time the colors gradually become darker; the flesh tints particularly take a reddish yellow color, by which the truth of the picture is very much injured. The fault is in the oil with which the colors are made, for all kinds of oil become yellow in time. Nut oil is most commonly made use of, with which the colors are dissolved and ground, and which is drying in its nature.

Alkali of any kind should be cautiously applied, such as soap, pearlash, soda, if the picture is not varnished; but in experienced hands spirits of wine, oil of turpentine may be used to take out dirt or stains in the subject. Unvarnished pictures must not lie under treatment too long, or they will be liable to come up from the canvas.

TOOLS REQUIRED.

The tools required by the picture frame maker may soon be enumerated.

Miter Block.—This block is made to guide the saw in cutting up mouldings. It consists of a thick piece of wood glued in a good bottom, with saw cuts in it at an angle of 45 degrees, so that the moulding, when cut off, will form a square frame. Eighteen inches long will be found a convenient length. (See fig. 7.) Miter boxes, may be purchased of dealers in carpenter's tools of different sizes. Langdon's being favorably known to the trade.

FIG 7.—MITER BLOCK.

Shooting Board - This board is made with a ledge, screwed on at an angle of 45 degrees, and a flat run for the plane laid on its side. The use of the shooting board is to "shoot" or plane the ends of the mouldings to bring the miters close together. (See fig. 8, page 113.)

Shooting Planes.—Planes about 15 inches long, and the width 3¼, without handles, the plane iron without a guard, used for shooting the ends of the moldings on the shooting board. Smoothing and other planes are sometimes required.

Saws.—Those used for cutting up moldings are called tenon or back saws, and are supported at the back by a piece of brass or iron to prevent the thin blade of the saw from bending.

Hammers, various sizes, and not too heavy.

Chisels, different widths ; *Bradawls and Gimlets*, various sizes.

Screwdrivers, large and small.

In addition to which a few small tools, such as pincers, scissors, punches, squares, &c.

There must also be cut brads, from ½ to 3 inches long, picture rings of all sizes, nails, screws, &c. There is also a useful implement known as the Banks & Seger clamp, for clamping the frame while the corners are being secured. It is a useful and not costly implement, and is sold by dealers in tools.

Glue is also used, and as its strength is dependent upon quality, we will give a little information upon the subject, as the strength of the work is only secured by a good article.

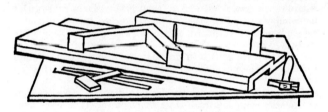

FIG. 8.—SHOOTING BOARD.

In applying glue, the hotter the glue the more force it will exert in keeping the united parts together ; it should, therefore, be applied immediately after boiling. Glue loses much of its strength by frequent re-melting. Glue should be purchased in dry weather, for that which is then soft is not of so good a quality as that which is crisp. The most transparent is the best. Good glue, if immersed in water for two or three days will not dissolve, but swell ; if of inferior quality it will partly or wholly dissolve. Again, that glue is the best which, being dissolved in water by heat, may be drawn into the thinest filament, and does not drop from the brush as oil or water, but when falling extends itself into threads. Glue made from the skin of old animals is much stronger than that of young ones.

PASTE.

Mix one tablespoonful of wheat flour with half a pint of cold water, adding the latter gradually, and thoroughly stirring in each portion before pouring in more, place the vessel over the fire and stir the whole assiduously until it boils ; great care should be taken to prevent caking or burning on the bottom.

An addition of half a teaspoonful of powdered alum will strengthen the product. The addition of a few grains of corrosive sublimate, or a few drops of creosote, will prevent it from turning mouldy and preserve it for years. When too hard or dry it may be softened by beating up with a little hot water.

MITERING PICTURE FRAMES.

In order to get instruction in the art of making picture frames, we will go into a shop where the frames are mitered together, fitted up, and turned out to be hung in cottage or mansion, and where all the frames from the gilder's shop adjoining come to be fitted up and completed. As we see two or three very busily engaged in various occcupations, we will not interupt them for the present, but take a critical survey of the shop. It is lighted by windows on two sides, and a stout wide bench runs under the windows round two sides of the room. At certain distances we see bench vises fastened, at some of which we see men busily at work. Down the middle of the shop is another wide bench, and on it we see rolls of engravings, and some are fitted into frames. At the end of the room is a small circular saw driven by the foot, and on the opposite side of the shop a good stock of moldings are arranged on bars let into the wall. We see four or five sizes and qualities of O. G. maple, a variety of patterns of inside slipping, beads, &c., in German moldings, and a good stock of moldings in the white ready to be joined before going to the gilder ; also gold moldings packed in white paper.

In a room adjoining this shop a man is seen busily employed packing a lot of pictures in cases ready to be sent out. The occupations of the men are various, and a division of labor seems to be the order of the day, as we see one actively employed in joining a large lot of maple frames with a large number down by his side ; another is "shooting" the moulding, while a third is cutting up mouldings. But we see a man in the center of the shop looking over a book, and as he has a good natured open countenance we will draw near and see what he will say to us in answer to inquiries as to what his occupation generally is. He informs us that he is constantly employed in "fitting up" all the best of the miscellaneous work, and that in consequence of his work requiring great care he does not get through so much. He fits up the gold frames finished in the gilder's shop with expensive chromos, proof engraving, oleographs, and oil paintings ; he also fits up the best work in water-color drawings, and is trusted with proofs and pictures to mount.

He informed us that he was called a "fitter-up," and that it was not his work to make frames, although he might be able to do it, and as he had satisfied himself as to the work in hand, he was about to hand the book over to a man in another room who did "mitering-up," and he offered to show us the way.

Our friend, the "fitter-up," not aware we had been engaged for a number of years in gilding and in a fine art repository, so treated us to a sight of some of the best chromos he was fitting up, little thinking they were old acquaintances, and that we had times before taken a pride in turning them out as he would do—first class.

We were received by the man about to execute the orders in the book, with civility, and as we stayed with him some time we will describe the execution of the work required.

As "Frith's Derby Day," was wanted at once, he set to work to cut out out the best O. O. G. maple, with a broad gold flat and hollow inside and the picture mounted on a stretcher The sight-edge of the inside gold, to allow of the requsite margin, must be 57¼ by 29, and unpapering some broad gold, flat and hollow, he carefully cut out on the saw block four pieces a little longer than the required length to allow of "shooting." He next selected some of the best maple, O. O. G., and cut one end off on the saw block to the required angle. He next took one of the pieces of gold flat and hollow, and placed it on the rabbet of the maple, and marked the length a little beyond the gold flat, and cut of the length. This he did with the three other sides. The "shooting board" was next required, when he placed the first maple in position. and with his plane, which had a good edge, took off enough to secure a good surface, and in the next place a clean top edge to the moldings. The next piece selected for the same operation was the piece corresponding in length, and after planing to his satisfaction, he measured the two pieces by putting the two sight edges together and making them exactly of a length.

Before shooting the gold flat and hollow, he said he should put the maple together so that he could more easily make the miters in both to run straight,

Taking the four pieces of molding, he went to the bench vise and fastened one of the long pieces therein with the rabbet outside, and the right hand very near the jaws of the vise. He next took up one of the short lengths on the left hand, and placed the two ends together. The two pieces were not placed exactly together, but the piece in the left hand was brought back from the sight edge about one-twentieth of an inch- When he had satisfied himself as to the exact position, holding the two tightly together, he, with a bradawl, decisively made a hole long enough to go into the molding in the vise.

When this was done he enlarged the hole in the piece he held

by a gimlet, so that the size cut brads would drive easily through
it without much friction or danger of splitting the wood. A little
thin glue was then applied and the molding placed together as
before, holding it very tightly together, when a brad of the requisite length, about 2½ inches long, was inserted and driven
home. In driving home the brad the molding held by the hand
was found to have moved forward a very little by the force of
the blows, and thus a capital miter was made ; a second brad was
then driven home and both punched below the surface. Had the
brad been driven home with the moldings exactly level this would
not have been the case.

The other two pieces were then joined in the same way.

Two miters having been made, two more remained to be put
together. He then took one-half of the frame and fastened it in
the vice near one of the unmitered ends, and with the assistance
of a lad on the other side of the bench he brought the two joined
pieces together in their proper places, and with the bradawl and
gimlet made the hole as above described ; he then took the half

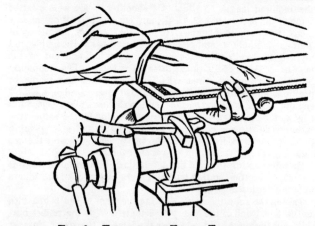

FIG. 9.—FITTING THE FRAME TOGETHER.

out of the vice and put in the other half in the same way and
made the hole in the fourth miter. He next glued the two ends
of the piece out of the vice, and with the help of the lad brought
the two halves together, and quickly and steadily drove home the
brad. The frame was then taken out of the vise, and the other
miter attended to in the same way and a second brad inserted,
and the two punched below the surface. The frame was again

put in the vice for the third miter to have a second brad driven in, when both was punched below the surface, and the frame was found to be well and neatly put together. Rather thin glue was used, and he was careful not to put too much on, so that it would appear on the top of the miters.

Sometimes with O. G. maple the lengths are found to be warp ed, and when cut into the required lengths by the picture frame maker and made up, the frame is found to be twisted and the miters bad. *Moldings should be kept flat before they are used.*

Having so far completed the maple frame, he at once proceeded to miter up the inside gold flat. Before taking it in hand he put on his left hand a glove made of chamois leather, explaining at the same time that in shooting and mitering up gold moldings, some of which were gilt down to the back edge, it was necessary to protect the gold from the heat of the hand, as inattention to this would be sure to damage a frame which was expected to be turned out in the best manner. He said also that a piece of soft cloth was glued down on the shooting board to prevent any scratches on the gold, and that he was particular to keep it free from shavings and grit.

After seeing to his plane-iron, the gold flat was soon ready for mitering, and it was noticeable that he was very particular to get the length of the pieces so that the frame would just take half of the rabbet, and the miters by that means would range exactly. With his left hand still covered by a glove, he handled the mold ing and mitered it up in the same way as before mentioned for the maple frame, and when completed the miters looked like a hair.

He next took the rabbet measure of the frame just mitered, and at once proceeded to cut out a stretcher from a large number of lengths of pine cut ready for the purpose.

In marking out the stuff for the stretcher he explained that there was no waste as in an ordinary molding, as the length was cut from one side and the other, avoiding the cutting out of the triangular piece necessary to make the miter. He also informed us that he knew it was the fashion in many country shops to make a stretcher by halving it together, but that a mitered stretcher was stronger, more expeditiously made, and was much neater than those made in such a way.

He then "shot" the lengths as usual, and soon put them together in the vise as before described, not troubling to put any slips into the vise to protect the pieces, and fitted it into its place in the rabbet of the gold flat.

The three frames placed one in the other was ready to go in to the fitter up.

When gold moldings are mitered down the back edge, it will

be necessary to lay in the vise some slips of wood covered with cloth to prevent marking the molding.

We have described mitering up a large frame, but smaller ones will not require the gimlet to be used before joining, as there is not the danger of the molding splitting where small brads are used.

Gilt slipping or inside edging for the inside of the maple, rose-wood, oak, or other frames, requires care in mitering up, owing to the thinness of the wood. In mitering sometimes the wood will split, therefore the brads selected must not be too large, and the mitered pieces must be handled tenderly till the glue is dry. Where it is twisted or warped it is almost impossible to make a neat miter, which is often the case with German moldings.

MOUNTING PICTURES.

A picture badly mounted is oftentimes a source of annoyance to its possessor, and spoils what might be otherwise a good subject. A picture of little value, if neatly mounted, really looks superior to one of greater value where little care has been bestowed upon it.

Engravings, chromos, photographs, oleographs, each require to be treated in a different manner, and we will describe what should be done to make them look well and preserve them in good condition for a great length of time.

ENGRAVINGS.

If it is an ordinary engraving it is best to prepare a stretcher as before recommended, by mitering up, and stretch evenly thereon a piece of muslin by means of tacks round the edge. The tacks should not be too wide apart or the calico will not be so firm.

The engraving is laid on the bench face uppermost, and the edge of the stretcher laid across it from edge of the picture, when, with a rule, the width of both margins can be ascertained. By halving this the exact width of margin can be seen, and marking the picture in two places on each side a straight edge can be used and a line drawn where the picture must be cut. The margin on the top and bottom of the engraving can be easily decided, as the top must be measured off the same width as the sides, and the bottom can be marked by putting the edge of the stretcher on the top line and marking the picture by the other edge of the stretcher. The engraving when cut, is just the size of the stretcher.

On a good smooth surface, sheets of clean paper should be laid, and the engraving turned over on its face. With a clean sponge and water go over the back of the picture till it has absorbed almost as much water as it will take, when, after lying in the water a short time a good coat of paste must be laid on very evenly, taking care that it contains no particles of grit. The stretcher must be evenly laid on and well rubbed down by the hand over the muslin at the back of the stretcher. The picture now on the stretcher can be turned up, and with a clean sheet of paper in the left hand laid on the outsides of the picture, rub well down on the stretcher.

Should there be any grit under the picture, which will be easily seen by the unevenness of the surface, it would be advisable to pull up the picture from one corner and remove it. If there is any dirt on the margin now is the time to remove it by applying the sponge with clean water, or it will not be removable when dry. Stains must be removed before mounting. The frame should be ready to receive the stretcher, and it should at once be tacked in and stood up to dry. If not tacked into the frame the stretcher will twist with the drying of the picture, which tacking in the frame prevents.

Should the engraving be on India paper it will not be advisable to damp it so much nor let it lie in the paste, but proceed as quickly as possible, as the India paper sometimes comes up, when it is a difficult matter to lay it again properly.

Many other pictures are mounted in the same manner as before mentioned, but where it is an old engraving, stained and discolored, it will be necessary to clean it before mounting.

Where gilt slipping is laid in a maple or other wood frame, the stretcher may be omitted by mounting the picture on the inside slipping in the following manner :—The picture must be well damped with a sponge and clean water. The frame made of slipping must be well glass-papered down, and glued and laid on the picture in its proper place and well rubbed down. When dry it will be found to be well stretched, and the gilt will go under the glass. It should be tacked in the frame to dry, and when fitted up a backboard used. This method is not suitable for large pictures.

PROOFS.

Sometimes valuable artist proof pictures come into the hands of the picture frame maker, with special directions as to their mounting, &c., as many gentlemen are most particular not to allow the fine lines of the engraving to be touched, and on no account to be pasted on the back.

When this is the case the proof must be carefully measured up for the stretcher as before mentioned, and marked on the back, but not cut. It must then be turned on its face on soft tissue paper, and moderately damped with clean sponge and water. The stretcher, covered with paper, must now be laid on the back of the proof in the place where it is meant to be mounted, and the outside edges must be glued and turned over on to the back of the stretcher, and well rubbed down and tacked into the frame. It will dry, and present a well-stretched picture, and the paper used will prevent the wood of the stretcher from staining a valuable picture, and keep the dust from the back. If it is important that the proof should not touch the glass it will be necessary to have two rabbets to the frame—one for the glass and the other for the picture.

PHOTOGRAPHS.

Photographs are usually mounted on card-board, and the great fault is that the majority are on thin board, and through bad mounting the picture is pulled out of shape, and it is difficult to fit it upon the frame to present a workman-like appearance.

The photograph should first be squared up by cutting the edges with a sharp knife guided by a straight-edge, when it should be put into clean water for an hour or two, and laid between blotting paper for a short time before mounting. Some thin *starch* should then be made and brushed over the back of the photogragh very evenly, which is then laid on the board so as to give equal margin. After well rubbing down with a sheet of paper it should be laid in a press or under weight to dry. If it is required to mount a picture with cold starch it will be found to roll under the brush, and the fingers of the right hand will best rub on an even coat.

Where a cut mount is ordered the photograph may be mounted on cardboard a little larger than the picture, placed behind the cut out mount and pasted in its place.

WATER COLORS AND CHROMOS.

Water colors require careful treatment, as it is not advisable to make them wet by paste, or the colors may be affected. After careful squaring up, the edges should be gone over with thin glue, and laid in its place on the mounting board. If a cut out mount is required it must be placed in front of the mounted water color.

Chromo lithographs do not require the care advisable for water colors ; the colors on the picture being oil, will not readily be disturbed. They may be mounted with thick paste and laid under pressure, and if a cut out mount is necessary the mounted picture must be pasted in its place at the back of it. The edges of the front card are cut slanting toward the picture, and may be brushed with gold size rather thin and real gold powder or good bronze put on with good effect.

OLEOGRAPHS.

Oleographs are pictures printed in oil color to represent oil paintings, and are mounted in the following manner. A stretcher is made the size of the picture with wedges at the corners as oil paintings. It is then covered with a smooth stout canvas or unbleached Holland, when the picture receives a coat of thin glue, the stretcher is laid on the picture and well rubbed down and left to dry. The stretchers should be stouter than ordinary as they require to be strong. After the picture is dry two coats of parchment size is laid on and then varnished with mastic.

These pictures are sometimes mounted as chromos with margin, and many subjects look very well.

MAPS.

Good muslin or fine canvas must be strained on a smooth clean board by tacks, and the map damped with a clean sponge on its back, and then well pasted, taking care that the edges are well saturated. The map must then be laid on the canvas, a sheet of paper on the top, and well rubbed down ; when dry two coats of parchment size must be laid on, and one or two coats of paper varnish When thoroughly dry the tacks may be taken out and the maps squared up with a straight-edge and knife, enough canvas being left on the top and bottom to attach to rollers. The sides are then bound with silk ribbon and the bottom tacked on to a roller, while on the top a moulding is usually secured. Sometimes the roller is cut in half and the map secured between by screws at the back.

Where the map is in several sheets they must be carefully joined in mounting, and edges well rubbed down, or the varnish may get under and stain the paper.

MARGIN, MOUNTS, FITTING UP, ETC.

There has hitherto been no rule for the width of margin on pictures, but it is usual to give a good broad margin to a valuable work of art, such as water colors, chromos, proof engravings, and even photographs looks best with a good margin. We have seen pictures framed with narrow margins according to the whim of their owner, and it has very much taken away from their appearance when framed. Common pictures or pictures of but little value do not require wide margins, and in measuring up pictures for framing this should be borne in mind. Engravings with

India paper are usually measured for a margin beyond, and where there is no India paper the picture is measured for the top and two sides to be equal, and the bottom margin considerably more to allow for the title.   The plate mark on the picture sometimes is a guide.   Large subjects require broader margins than small ones.

Water colors and chromos can be measured up for equal margin all round, as also photographs if the margin is wide, but should it be narrow a little deeper margin may be left at the bottom.

There is a circumstance which sometimes decides the width of margin at the bottom of the subject, and that is if the picture measures nearly square it is measured up so as to bring the frame a little longer, as many dislike a square frame.

MOUNTING BOARDS AND MOUNTS.

Mounting and card board may be had almost any size and quality.   Mounting boards, technically so called, are commoner than card boards, as they will be found on examination to have an inferior brown paper for the inside of the board, while the cardboards are white throughout and a whiter and better surface, Cut out mounts are usually made of the latter.

Mounts, with or without gold line and bevel, may be had of any size, quality, or pattern.   Sizes suitable for photographs are often required.

CLEANING ENGRAVINGS.

The frame-maker, in receiving orders for frames, is sometimes required to clean the engravings before putting them into the frame.   Valuable old pictures are often discolored with age, smoke, dirt and dust, so that the title is scarcely legible, and the picture lost in the stained condition of the paper.   A method that will be effective and still preserve the lines of the engraving perfect, will prove valuable when it is required.

The engraving must be laid down on a smooth board, with a clean sheet of paper underneath, and with a clean sponge and water carefully wet the picture on both sides, and then saturate it well with a soft sponge with the following mixture: ¼ lb. chloride of lime, 2 oz. oxalic acid, 1 quart of water.

The above will be known to be the right strength by its turning a magenta color.

The application must continue as long as there is any stain to come out, and then sponged freely both sides with clean water. We have cleaned engravings so stained and yellow that the picture could scarcely be distinguished.   The paper looked as clean as when it was made, and the engraving stood out brilliant on its new back ground.

We must caution those who try this receipt not on any account to use it on water color drawing or prints that have been colored with water color, as in the first instance a clean sheet of paper would be left plain. This receipt will not touch any color that has been mixed with oil, as is the case with the ink the picture is printed with. The above receipt loses its virtue when it has been made some time.

FITTING-UP.

A picture badly fitted up will get discolored with the air and dust, and will not look so well as if a little more care and time had been spent upon it.

When the frame is made and the picture mounted it is ready for fitting up, when the glass must be cut, care being taken to select a piece free from defects.

Cutting glass is easily accomplished with a little practice, but some of the foreign is brittle, and will sometimes crack across the pane instead of the cut. The *modus operandi* is as follows A large pane is placed on the board covered with green baize, and looked over to see there are no defects, when the frame is measured and the the straight-edge is placed on the glass, making due allowance for the room the diamond takes up in cutting. A steady cut is given, holding it between the first and second fingers of the right hand, and keeping it inclined toward the arm. Then if it is a long cut on a large piece of glass the best way will be to bring the cut to the edge of the board, and with a steady downward jerk of the piece in hand (if the cut has been perfect) the glass will part evenly. With smaller pieces it will part by holding the glass with the finger and thumb of each hand on each side of the cut, and using a little downward force.

When the pane has been cut the required size it must be well cleaned both sides with whitening, and fastened into the frame by pasting strips of paper and laying them in so that one half lies on the glass and the other on the side of the rabbet but not to show in front of course. When this is dry it will be firm and no dust can get in. The picture is then cut to the required size, attention being given that the margin is right all the way round. As this is a matter of some little difficulty to the amateur we will just say it can be quickly done by measuring the inside of the frame and then by putting the rule across the picture you will see how much the margin on the two sides measure, when by taking one-half and marking it off on the picture and drawing a line across as a guide for cutting, the margin will be found to be equal. The picture must be measured in the same way for the two other margins. When it is cut it will be found to go into the frame exact with the margin correct. If, on measurement, it should be found a little out, a strip cut from the opposite side where the margin is narrow will rectify the error.

If it is a medium-sized picture a back-board will fasten it in. Back-boards can be had of any thickness. The back-board is cut to the required size, and if not wide enough is glued up with a piece of the required size, and, when dry, it is planed up and outside edges beveled.

Now that the glass is pasted in, the picture cut to the proper size, and the back-board ready, it can be bradded in, but before this is done it will be necessary to see that the glass is quite clean on the inside, that no dust or small particle of wood is between the glass and the picture, and also that the picture is laid in its proper place, when the back can be put in and bradded up. It is advisable to put two or three brads in each side, and then satisfy yourself by inspection that everything is right, or you may have to take out the whole of the brads again to remove a particle of dust or shaving.

The picture must now be backed up with brown paper, or narrow slips pasted round the edge of the back.

If it is to be backed up with brown paper the sheet must be cut the size required and damped with a wet sponge. The back edge of the frame must be thinly glued and the paper at once strained on. This will strengthen the frame, keep the dust out, and perhaps hide a back-board not very smooth.

Strips of colored paper look clean pasted round when a smooth back-board is in the frame. Where stretchers are used they are backed up in both ways, according to fancy.

If it is a large picture on mounting board a panneled back-board would be desirable.

In fitting up maple and gold frames, the inside gold must be blocked in tight, and when the gold is ordered under the glass, the glass must first be cut. The stretcher with the mounted picture will be bradded in last, and the back papered up. With maple, rosewood, or any French-polished frames, it is necessary to clean them down with a reviver before sending them out, as in handling the molding it becomes dull. Receipts will be found at the end of this volume.

OXFORD FRAMES.

These frames have become favorites within the last few years. They are made of oak with cross corners and are got up in fancy patterns, some of which are finished with ultramarine on the bevels. They can be had of the wholesale houses of assorted sizes.

They should be rubbed over with linseed oil, which will give the wood a richer appearance.

FRENCH POLISHING AND VARNISHING.

Frames made to order, of oak and other wood, require French polishing or varnishing, when it will be convenient to know how to lay on a lasting and brilliant polish. The following precise directions, if followed, will give a satisfactory result.

FRENCH POLISHING.

The mode of application necessary for French polish differs from that of ordinary varnishes, being effected by rubbing it with a fine cloth upon the surface of the material to be polished and using oil and spirits of wine during the process. In applying it to large surfaces use a rubber formed of a flat coil of thick woolen cloth, such as drugget, &c., which may be *torn* off the piece in order that the surface of the rubber, which is made of the torn edge of the cloth, may be soft and pliant, and not hard and stiff as would be the case were it to be cut off, and therefore be liable to scratch the soft surface of the varnish. This rubber is to be securely bound with thread to prevent it from uncoiling when it is used, and it may vary in its size from one to three inches in diameter and from one to two inches in thickness, according to the extent of the surface to be varnished. The varnish is to be applied to the middle of the flat face of the rubber by shaking up the bottle containing it against the rubber; it will absorb a considerable quantity and will continue to supply it equally and in due proportion to the surface which is undergoing the process of polishing. The face of the rubber must next be covered by a soft linen cloth doubled, the remainder of the cloth being gathered together at the back of the rubber to form a handle to hold it by, and the face of the cloth must be moistened with a little raw linseed oil applied upon the finger to the middle of it, and the operation be commenced by quickly and lightly rubbing the surface of the article to be polished in a constant succession of small circular strokes, if a flat surface, but if a molded face a light back and forward stroke without lifting the hand will answer, and the operation must be confined to a space of not more than ten or twelve inches square until such space is finished, when an adjoining one may be commenced and united with the first, and so on until the whole surface is covered. The varnish is enclosed by the double fold of cloth, which by absorption, becomes merely moistened with it, and the rubbing of each piece must be continued until it becomes nearly dry. The rubber may, for a second coat, be wetted with varnish without the oil, and applied as before. A third coat may also be given in the same manner ; then a fourth with a little oil, which must be followed as before, with two others without oil ; and thus proceeding until the varnish acquires some thickness, which will be after a few repetitions, and depends on the care that has been taken in finishing the surface. Then a little spirits of wine may be applied to the inside of the rubber after wetting it with the varnish and being covered with the linen as before ; it must be very quickly and uniformly rubbed over every part of the surface ; this tends to make it even, and very much conduces to its polish. The cloth must next be wetted with a little spirits of wine and oil without varnish, and the surface being rubbed over, with the precautions last mentioned, until it is nearly dry, the effect of the operation will be seen, and if it be found that it is not complete the process must be continued, with the introduction of spirits of wine in its turn as directed, until the surface becomes uniformly smooth and beautifully polished. The work to be polished should be placed opposite the light in order that the effect of the polishing may be better seen. In this manner a surface from one to eight feet square may be polished, and the process, instead of being limited to the polishing of rich cabinets or other smaller works, can now be applied to tables and other large pieces of furniture with very great advantages over the common method of polishing with wax, oils, &c. In some cases it is considered preferable to rub the wood over with a little oil applied on a linen cloth before begining to polish, but the propriety of this method is very much doubted. When the color of the wood to be polished is dark a harder polish may be made by making the composition of one part of shellac and eight parts of spirits, proceeding as before directed. For work polished by the French-polish, the recesses or carved work, or where the surfaces are not liable to wear, or are difficult to be got at with the rubber, a spirit made without lac, and considerably thicker than that used in the foregoing process, may be applied to those parts with a brush or hair pencil, as is commonly done in other modes of varnishing. French polish is not proper for dining tables nor for anything where it is liable to be partially exposed to a considerable heat.

STOPPING FOR FRENCH POLISHING.

Plaster-of-paris, when made into a creamy paste, with water, proves a most valuable pore-filling material. It is to be rubbed

by means of a coarse rag across the woody fiber into the holes
and pores till they be completely saturated, and then the superfluous stucco on the outside is to be instantly wiped off.   The
succeeding processes are technically termed papering, oiling, and
embodying.

When finely-pounded whiting is mixed with painter's drying
oil, it constitutes another good pore-filler.   It is applied in the
same manner as the preceding one, and it is recommended on
account of its quickly hardening and tenacious virtues as a cement ; sometimes white lead is used in lieu of whiting.

Before using either of these, or other compositions for the same
purpose, it is best to tint them to correspond exactly with the
color of the article it is intended to size.

Holes and crevices may be well filled up with a cement that is
made by melting beeswax in combination with resin and shellac.

VARNISHING.

Flat camel's hair or hog's hair brushes are generally used for
varnishing, and usually come varying in width one to four inches.
Turned and carved work require small tools to go over the members and sweeps.   The best way to preserve them is to rinse them
after use in spirits of turpentine, wash in warm soap-suds and
hang them up in a dry place where no air is moving.

Where the brushes have been neglected they must be soaked
in varnish for an hour or two, but if wanted immediately they
can be softened in turpentine.   For fancy work a good sponge
will sometimes be found preferable.

The varnish dish should be provided with a closely-fitting lid,
and a wire strained across the dish to scrape the brush over when
dipped, or too much will be laid on.

After dipping, the brush should be passed over the wire, and
the first coat may be laid on across the grain of the wood as
evenly as possible, but in the finishing the varnish must be laid
on with the grain.   The tool should be lightly handled and not
slowly used, as some varnishes set very quickly.   Varnishers
sometimes make a ground with a rubber full of French polish
before the application of the spirit varnish.   The rubber must
be thoroughly dry before the application of the varnish.   The
last coat applied should stand some time before receiving the
fine varnish.   It should be finished off with a damp rubber   The
above will give brilliant and lasting work.

CHOICE OF HAIR TOOLS.

Round and flat brushes are used, but the flat are more useful.
They should be neatly made and yet very strong, and the hair

should not be cut at the points, but smooth to the touch. They should also be very elastic, springing back to their shape when in use, and the hair should be silky-looking. There should be no diverging hairs, but their shape should be wedge-like. Polished cedar handles ensure thorough cleaning, and they are more pleasant to use.

Sable tools should come to a firm fine point, and the hair must be of a pale yellow cast. They can be had both flat and round.

Badger tools are superior when the hair is light, long, and pliant, in color black with white ends. Instead of coming to a point the hairs diverge. They seldom want cleaning as used by gilders.

RULES FOR POLISHING.

Work to be dusted before commencing.

Every embodying must be allowed a proper time to harden and absorb before re-application of smoothing stuffs or polishes.

The rubber must be covered with a clean part of the rag at each wetting.

Rubbers must not be worked too long in the same direction, nor heavily laid on when wet, or the work will be streaky.

Marks of the rubber may be smoothed by working in an opposite direction with a rubber nearly dry.

Large surfaces should not be gone over all at once.

Fine linen makes the best rubber coverings. Cheap cotton will do as well after washing.

Carved work that has been finely varnished presents a brilliant appearance after cleaning with an oiled flannel.

The only fixed oil used in French polishing is raw linseed oil.

Polishing rubbers should be preserved in close tin canisters.

Polishing and varnishing should be performed in a room, the temperature of which is about 50 degrees Fahrenheit, and it should be free from damp

The most convenient way of laying matt or burnish gold size on small work is to lay two or three brushfuls on the back of the left hand when it will be found that the brush can be filled and brought to a fine point very quickly, and the size is kept in a workable condition by the heat of the hand.

USEFUL RECEIPTS.

Compo.—One pound of glue must be dissolved in one gallon of water. In another kettle boil together 2 lbs. of resin, 1 gill of Venice turpentine, and 1 pint of linseed oil ; mix all together in one kettle, and boil and stir till the water has evaporated. Turn the whole into a tub of finely rolled whiting, and work it until it is of the consistence of dough.

ANOTHER RECEIPT.—Boil 7 lbs. of the best glue in 3¼ pints of water. Melt 3 lbs. of white resin in 3 pints of raw linseed oil. When the above have been well boiled put them in a large vessel and simmer them for half an hour, stirring the mixture and taking sure that it does not boil over. The whole must then be turned into a box of whiting rolled and sifted, and mix till it is of the consistence of dough.

POLISH REVIVER.—Quarter pint of linseed oil, 2 ozs. wood naptha, 1 oz. spirits of salts.

BOOKBINDERS' VARNISH.—Quarter pint of methy. spirits, 1 oz. gum juniper, 1 oz. orange shellac.

PARTIALLY RESILVERING.—The silvering must be removed from the injured part, and the glass cleaned thoroughly. A wall of beeswax must be formed round the spot, and nitrate of silver poured on, and the silver precipitated by oil of cloves and spirits of wine. This method is said to be most successful.

BRUSH POLISH.—The following receipt must be used warm, and laid on with a brush. If the article to be polished be held to the fire before the application a better polish will be the result : 2 ozs. shellac, 2 ozs. white resin, dissolved in one pint of spirits of wine will be found to answer well for carved work or Oxford frames.

FRENCH POLISH REVIVER.—Half pint linseed oil, 1 oz. of spirits of camphor, 2 ozs. vinegar, ½ oz. of butter of antimony, ¼ oz. of spirits of hartshorn.

ANOTHER.—One lb. of naptha, 4 ozs. of shellac, ¼ oz. oxalic acid. Let it stand till dissolved, and add 3 ozs. of linseed oil.

GOLD INK.—24 leaves gold, ½ oz. bronze gold, 30 drops of spirits of wine, 30 grains of honey, 4 drams gum-arabic, 4 ozs. rain water. The gold must be rubbed with the gum and honey, and the whole mixed with water, and the spirit added.

Gold and silver inks used for illumination, are simply the metals powdered very fine, and mixed in weak gum water. Gold leaf ground with honey and mixed with thin gum, will be found to work well for illuminations.

GILDER'S ORMOLU.—Quarter pint spirits wine, ½ oz. garnet shellac, 1 dram of red saurders wood, ¼ dram turmeric.

TO CLEAN LOOKING GLASSES.—Sponge down the glass with gum and water, equal parts, then dust down with whiting, and finish with a soft old silk handkerchief.

TO CLEAN MARBLE.— Mix with ¼ pint of soft soap, ½ gill of turpentine, sufficient pipe clay and bullock's gall to make the whole into a rather thick paste. Apply it to the marble with a soft brush, and after a day or two, when quite dry, rub it off with a soft rag. Apply this a second or third time till the marble is quite clean.

GOLD COLOR COPAL VARNISH.—Take one ounce of powdered copal, two ounces of essential oil of lavender, and six ounces of spirits of turpentine ; put the oil of lavender into a matrass of a proper size placed on a sand bath subjected to a moderate heat. When the oil is very warm add the copal from time to time in very small quantities, and stir the mixture with a stick of white wood rounded at the end. When the copal has entirely disappeared put in the turpentine in almost a boiling state at three different times, and keep continually stirring the mixture until the solution be quite completed.

CLEANING ENGRAVINGS.—Put the engraving on a smooth board, cover it thinly with common salt finely powdered. Squeeze lemon juice upon the salt so as to dissolve a considerable portion of it ; elevate one end of the board so that it may form an angle of about 45 or 50 degrees. Pour on the engraving boiling water from a tea kettle until the salt and lemon juice be all washed off. The engraving then will be perfectly clean and free from stains. It must be dried on the board or some smooth surface gradually. If dried by the fire or the sun it will be tinged with a yellow color.

Another Method.—Immerse the print for an hour or so in a ley made by adding to the strongest muriatic acid its own weight in water, and to three parts of this mixture adding one of red oxide of manganese.

A print, if not properly clean may remain in this liquid for twenty-four hours without harm. Indian ink stains should in the first instance be assisted out with hot water ; pencil marks taken out with Indian rubber so carefully as not to injure the engraving. If the print has been mounted, the paste on the back should be thoroughly removed with warm water. The saline crystal left by the solution may be removed by repeated rinsings in warm water.

INK SPOTS IN MAHOGANY.—To take out ink spots in mahogany, apply oxalic acid in water with a sponge till the ink disappears.

TO REVIVE THE GILT OF PICTURE FRAMES.—Beat up three ozs. of the whites of eggs with one oz. of chloride of potash or soda. Brush the frame carefully over with the above, when the frame will have a much fresher appearance.

TO TAKE INK OUT OF PAPER.—Two drams of muriate of tin mixed with double its quantity of water applied with a soft brush, will bring out the ink. The paper must be well rinsed in water to wash off the stain.

Another.—Citric or tartaric acids can be applied to the leaves of books or engravings to take out ink stains.

To REMOVE STAINS AND SPOTS FROM PAPER.—The clear solution of chloride of lime diluted with twice its bulk of water, will effectually and expeditiously remove stains from prints and printed paper. First soak the paper in clear water till it becomes smooth, then remove it into a dish large enough to hold it flat filled with the solution diluted as above. The stain will disappear in a few minutes, after that again soak the paper in clear water to free it from chloride of lime, and dry it between sheets of blotting paper.

To TAKE GREASE AND INK OUT OF PAPER.—Apply to it a camel's hair pencil dipped in muriate of tin, two drams, water four drams. After the writing has disappeared the paper should be passed through water and then dried. To extract grease spots from paper, gently warm the greased or spotted part of the paper, and then press upon it pieces of blotting paper one after another to absorb as much of the grease as possible. Have ready some fine clear spirits of turpentine, heated almost to boiling state ; slightly warm the greased part of the paper, and with a soft clean brush, wet both sides of the spot with the heated turpentine. By repeating this application the grease will be extracted. Lastly, with another brush, dipped in rectified spirits of wine, go over the place, and the grease will entirely disappear without the paper being discolored.

WHITE FURNITURE CREAM.—With the following receipt the vinegar must be mixed with the linseed oil by degrees, and the bottle well shook up. The spirit of antimony must afterward be added, and well mixed. Six ounces of raw linseed oil, three ozs. methylated spirits, three ozs. white wine vinegar, half an ounce of butter of antimony.

CEMENT FOR MOUNTING PHOTOGRAPHS.—Fine wheat starch, four drams, beat into a paste with cold water, one oz. of best Russian glue ; dissolve in a pint of boiling water ; while boiling pour on the starch ; put the whole into a saucepan, and boil till as thick as treacle. When required for use a small quantity is to be melted in a little warm water.

BRUSHES FOR VARNISHING.—Varnish brushes should be made of long white hairs, have a good spring, and be of the best quality. They should be worn flat, sharp, and thin at the point, as they will lay on the varnish so much more regularly. No oil brush should be put in the varnish, if so they should be well washed first in turpentine and well squeezed out. It is important to pay a little attention to brushes when not in use, and oil varnish brushes should be *suspended* in varnish of the same sort as used, care being taken that the varnish covers the hairs of the brush up to the binding of the tin. The advantage is that they are always clean, pliable, and straight. If brushes are kept in turpentine they become hard and harsh, and the turpentine left in the brush will cause the work to look cloudy or streaked.

To SILVER COPPER WORK.—Dissolve in one ounce of aquafortis, over a moderate fire, one dram of good silver in small pieces, when dissolved take the vessel off the fire, and throw in as much white tartar as will absorb the liquor, and make it into a paste. Copper or brass work cleaned and rubbed over with this paste will have a brilliant silver surface.

To REMOVE VARNISH FROM PRINTS.—The varnish may sometimes be removed by rubbing it up with the fingers; a white powder is produced, which must be dusted off. The print must then be stretched, sized and varnished, as before directed. If the varnish will not rise by rubbing, it has not been varnished with mastic.

Another Method.—Blotting paper spread over the print and saturated with pure spirit, will dissolve the varnish. The blotting paper should be changed and the process repeated if not effectual the first or second time.

WOOD STAINING.—Many of the cheap frames now sold are stained wood, and walnut is imitated by darkening elm or beech. The more figure there is on the wood the better beech may be made to imitate mahogany by the following receipt :—One ounce of dragon's blood, pulverized, put into one pint of rectified spirits of wine ; keep it in a warm place until dissolved.

Oak stain may soon be made by adding to a quart of water two ounces each of potash and pearlash. This is a very good stain, but should be used carefully, as it blisters the hands and softens brushes. It should be kept corked up. A lighter stain may be made by adding more water.

To improve the tint of any stain mix one ounce of nitric acid, half a tea-spoonful of muriatic acid, quarter of an ounce of grain tin, and two ounces of rain water. It should be kept in a well corked bottle, and mixed two days before using. A little of the above will render any stain more brilliant.

IMITATING ROSEWOOD.—1. A transparent liquid rose pink, used in imitating rosewood, consists in mixing ¼ lb. of potash in 1 gallon of hot water, and ¼ lb. of red sanders wood is added thereto ; when the color of the wood is extracted, 2½ lbs. of gum shellac are added and dissolved over a quick fire ; the mixture is then ready to be used on a groundwork made with logwood stain.

2. Boil ½ lb. of logwood in 3 pints of water till it is of a very dark red, add ¼ oz. of salts of tartar. While boiling hot stain the

wood with two or three coats, taking care that it is nearly dry between each ; then with a stiff flat brush, such as is used by the painters for graining, form streaks with black stain. This imitation will very nearly equal the appearance of dark rosewood.

3. Stain with black stain, and when dry, with a brush as above dipped in the brightening liquid, form red veins in imitation of the grain of rosewood. A handy brush for the purpose may be made out of a flat brusn, such as is used for varnishing ; cut the sharp points off, and make the edges irregular by cutting out a few hairs here and there, and you will have a tool which will actually imitate the grain.

BLACK STAIN.—Boil 1 lb. of logwood in 4 quarts of water, add a double handful of walnut peel or shells ; boil it up again, take out the chips, add a pint of the best vinegar, and it will be fit for use ; apply it boiling. This will be improved, if when dry, a solution of green copperas, an ounce to a quart of water, is applied hot over the first stain.

BLACK STAIN FOR IMMEDIATE USE. Boil ½ lb. of chip logwood in 2 quarts of water, add 1 oz. of pearlash, and apply it hot to the work with a brush. Then take ½ lb. of logwood, boil it as before in 2 quarts of water, and add ½ oz. of verdigris and ¼ oz of copperas ; strain it off, put in ½ lb. of rusty steel filings ; with this go over the work a second time.

EBONY STAINS.—1. Stain work with the black stain, adding powdered nutgall to the logwood and copperas solution, dry, rub down well, oil, then use French polish made tolerably dark with indigo, or finely-powdered stone blue.

2. Hold an ordinary slate over gas, lamp, or candle, until it is well smoked at the bottom, scrape a sufficient quantity into French polish, and well mix ; then polish the article in the ordinary way. If there are any lumps gently rub them down and apply another coat.

3. Prepare a decotion of logwood by adding a small handful of chips to a pint of rain water. Allow this to simmer until reduced one-fourth, and while the liquor is hot, dress the work to be ebonized two or three times. To the remainder of the liquor add two bruised nut-galls, a few very rusty nails, bits of iron hooping, or a piece of sulphate of iron the size of a walnut, and as much more rain water as will make about three-quarters of a pint of liquor. Apply this, which will be a black stain, hot as before, giving two coats, and when thoroughly dry, polish with ordinary French polish, to which sufficient powdered thumb-blue has been added to preceptibly color the polish. Use a glazed pipkin in which to prepare the stain. Take care that no oil or grease comes in contact with the brushes used or the surface of the wood until

ready for polishing. Let each coat of stain dry before the next is added, and rub down with well used, fine glass-paper. Sycamore, chestnut, and plane-tree, are the best woods for ebonizing in the above manner.

4. Infuse gall-nuts in vinegar in which rusty nails have been soaked, rub the wood with the infusion, dry, polish, burnish.

5. Stain in the first place with a hot saturated solution of logwood, containing a little alum ; and, when dry, brush it over with common writing ink.

IMITATION CARVED OAK FRAMES.—These frames may be made to look very effective with a gold inside, and are suitable for historical engravings.

They are made up from moldings in the white, and mounted with composition ornaments, backed up as if for gilding. After a coat of thin white, they must be glass-papered down, and then coated with Venetian red and white. Black Japan thinned down with turpentine, is then laid on, and combed for oak grain. Two coats of oak varnish will be required to finish the work. If a woody grain is required, mix chrome yellow with the color.

TO BRIGHTEN GOLD FRAMES.—Take sufficient flour of sulphur to give a golden tinge to about 1½ pints of water, and in this boil 4 or 5 bruised onions, or garlic, which will answer the same purpose ; strain off the liquid, and with it, when cold, wash with a soft brush any gilding which requires restoring, and when dry it will come out bright.

GOLD FRAMES.—Frames that have taken the dust and look dirty may be brightened by going over them with a soft sponge and water till the finish size is removed, and then size them again. This should be done by a practiced hand, or the gold may be rubbed off.

FRENCH POLISH.—To one pint of spirits of wine, and half an ounce of gum shellac, half an ounce of seed lac, and a quarter of an ounce of gum sandarach; submit the whole to a gentle heat, frequently shaking it, till the various gums are dissolved, when it is fit for use.

Another.—Shellac 6 ozs., naptha 1 quart, sandarach 1 oz., benzoin ¾ oz.

Another —Three ozs. shellac, ½ oz. of gum mastic pulverized, and one pint of methylated spirits of wine added. Let it stand till dissolved.

Another.—12 ozs. shellac, 2 ozs. gum elima, 3 ozs. gum copal, 1 gallon of spirits of wine ; dissolve.

Another.—The following must be well mixed and dissolved :— Pale shellac 2¼ lbs., 3 ozs. mastic, 3 ozs. sandarach, 1 gall. spirits of wine. After the above is dissolved, add 1 pint of copal varnish, 1¼ ozs. shellac, ½ oz. gum juniper, ¼ oz. benzoin, ½ pint of methylated alcohol.

Another.—Gum mastic, seedlac, sandarach, shellac, and gumarabic, 1 oz. each pulverize and add ¾ oz. of virgin wax. Dissolve in 1 quart of rectified spirits of wine.

STRENGTH OF GOLD SIZE.—As we before mentioned that reference would again be made to the strength of size, with a view of determining the right strength for the work, we will do so now at the end of the volume.

Hitherto experience has decided the strength of burnish gold size, so that when the burnisher is applied it will not friz up ; and even the man of experience is somewhat puzzled when he wishes to get on with his work, and has hot size to make up his preparations.

A few little experiments have been tried during the progress of this volume through the press with a view to determine, as near as can be, the strength required for a good burnish, without leaving it to an uncertainty.

There is a little instrument used to test milk called a *Lactometer*, which is a *float* that records the density of the milk.

By this little instrument the density and strength of size may always be known exactly, without leaving any doubt on the matter ; and as a standard to regulate the strength required, a good burnish will be the result of size where the float registers it a little weaker than three-quarters milk, and matt a little stronger. Matt should be stronger, and the float would register near the 2.

STATE OF OIL PAINTINGS TO BE LINED.—If an oil painting requires lining, and is badly cracked or very rotten, a good sheet of paper should be pasted on the face of the picture to strengthen and preserve it during the operation ; and the stretcher should be a little larger than the painting, so that the edges of the picture will not tear up. The sheet of paper must be carefully sponged off when the picture is dry.

Printed in the United Kingdom
by Lightning Source UK Ltd.
102698UKS00001B/22

9 781410 104014